A CHILD'S GARDEN OF VERSES AND OTHER POEMS

BY ROBERT LOUIS STEVENSON

PARENTS' MAGAZINE PRESS
A Division of Parents' Magazine Enterprises, Inc.
New York

Third Printing

Printed in the United States of America

Library of Congress Catalog Card Number: 64-15711

PREFACE

Here in this book are the first real poems to be written for the enjoyment of children. Who does not know such lines as "I have a little shadow that goes in and out with me . . ." or "The world is so full of a number of things . . ." and "How do you like to go up in a swing . . ."? Only Mother Goose rhymes are more familiar.

Stevenson wove into this poetry his early experiences and fancies, all so clearly remembered that the child himself seems to speak. The simple rhymes and rhythms have child-like appeal, and it is in their nature to remain in the memory, perhaps for a lifetime.

Their author is a beloved figure in our literature, the Scottish poet, story-writer, and essayist, born in Edinburgh, November 13, 1850. Boy and man, Robert Louis Stevenson struggled against illness through his whole span of forty-four brief years. In these pages are touching glimpses of the child who could not run and play with other boys.

"When I was sick and lay abed
I had two pillows at my head,
And all my toys beside me lay
To keep me happy all the day."

Stevenson led his soldiers, sailed his ships, and built his cities, all in imagination on the counterpane. With him was his nurse, Cummy, the wonderful person, Alison Cunningham, who brightened his dreary days, often with stories.

One lovely poem tells how the small boy played "at books that I have read, till it is time to go to bed." He was a hunter, watching the river, "by whose brink the roaring lions came to drink." Then he became an Indian scout who (round his parents) "prowled about."

"So, when my nurse comes in for me,
Home I return across the sea,
And go to bed with backward looks
At my dear land of Story-books."

The growing boy, never strong, traveled with his father and mother, then by himself, unable to stand the cold climate of Scotland for long. As Stevenson traveled he wrote, and prose and poetry of distinguished quality followed in his wake. *A Child's Garden of Verses* appeared in 1885. Although Stevenson's poems for children are his best known, this volume includes some of his other poems that demonstrate his remarkable versatility. The brawn of his spirit created the rugged adventures of *Treasure Island* and *Kidnapped*, as well as the sinister excitement of *Dr. Jekyll and Mr. Hyde*.

Stevenson spent the last four years of his life with his wife on a sunny Samoan island. There the admiring natives called him Tusitala, "teller of tales." The little boy in his *Child's Garden of Verses* never changed.

"If I could find a higher tree
Farther and farther I should see,
To where the grown-up river slips
Into the sea, among the ships,
To where the roads on either hand
Lead onward into fairy land."

IRENE SMITH
Former Superintendent of Work with Children
Brooklyn Public Library
Brooklyn, New York

PART I

A CHILD'S GARDEN OF VERSES

BY ROBERT LOUIS STEVENSON

ILLUSTRATED
BY
CHARLES
ROBINSON

CONTENTS

A CHILD'S GARDEN OF VERSES

THE CHILD ALONE

GARDEN DAYS

ENVOYS

TO ALISON CUNNINGHAM

from her boy

For the long nights you lay awake
And watched for my unworthy sake:
For your most comfortable hand
That led me through the uneven land:
For all the story books you read:
For all the pains you comforted:
For all you pitied, all you bore,
In sad and happy days of yore:—
My second Mother, my first Wife,
The angel of my infant life—
From the sick child, now well and old,
Take, nurse, the little book you hold!

And grant it, Heaven, that all who read
May find as dear a nurse at need,
And every child who lists my rhyme,
In the bright, fireside, nursery clime,
May hear it in as kind a voice
As made my childish days rejoice!

R. L. S.

A CHILD'S GARDEN OF VERSES

BED IN SUMMER

In winter I get up at night
And dress by yellow candlelight.
In summer, quite the other way,
I have to go to bed by day.

I have to go to bed and see
The birds still hopping on the tree,
Or hear the grown-up people's feet
Still going past me in the street.

And does it not seem hard to you,
When all the sky is clear and blue,
And I should like so much to play,
To have to go to bed by day?

A THOUGHT

It is very nice to think
The world is full of meat and drink,
With little children saying grace
In every Christian kind of place.

AT THE SEASIDE

When I was down beside the sea
A wooden spade they gave to me
  To dig the sandy shore.
My holes were empty like a cup,
In every hole the sea came up,
  Till it could come no more.

YOUNG NIGHT THOUGHT

ALL night long and every night,
When my mamma puts out the light,
I see the people marching by,
As plain as day, before my eye.

Armies and emperors and kings,
All carrying different kinds of things,
And marching in so grand a way,
You never saw the like by day.

So fine a show was never seen,
At the great circus on the green;
For every kind of beast and man
Is marching in that caravan.

At first they move a little slow,
But still the faster on they go,
And still beside them close I keep
Until we reach the town of Sleep.

WHOLE DUTY OF CHILDREN

A CHILD should always say what's true
And speak when he is spoken to,
And behave mannerly at table;
At least as far as he is able.

RAIN

THE rain is raining all around,
It falls on field and tree,
It rains on the umbrellas here,
And on the ships at sea.

PIRATE STORY

THREE of us afloat in the meadow by the swing,
  Three of us aboard in the basket on the lea.
Winds are in the air, they are blowing in the spring,
  And waves are on the meadow like the waves there are at sea.

Where shall we adventure, today that we're afloat,
  Wary of the weather and steering by a star?
Shall it be to Africa, a-steering of the boat,
  To Providence, or Babylon, or off to Malabar?

Hi! but here's a squadron a-rowing on the sea—
  Cattle on the meadow a-charging with a roar!
Quick, and we'll escape them, they're as mad as they can be,
  The wicket is the harbour and the garden is the shore.

FOREIGN LANDS

UP into the cherry tree
Who should climb but little me?
I held the trunk with both my hands
And looked abroad on foreign lands.

I saw the next door garden lie,
Adorned with flowers, before my eye,
And many pleasant places more
That I had never seen before.

I saw the dimpling river pass
And be the sky's blue looking glass;
The dusty roads go up and down
With people tramping in to town.

If I could find a higher tree
Farther and farther I should see,
To where the grown-up river slips
Into the sea among the ships,

To where the roads on either hand
Lead onward into fairy land,
Where all the children dine at five,
And all the playthings come alive.

WINDY NIGHTS

WHENEVER the moon and stars are set,
   Whenever the wind is high,
All night long in the dark and wet,
   A man goes riding by.
Late in the night when the fires are out,
Why does he gallop and gallop about?

Whenever the trees are crying aloud,
   And ships are tossed at sea,
By, on the highway, low and loud,
   By at the gallop goes he.
By at the gallop he goes, and then
By he comes back at the gallop again.

SINGING

Of speckled eggs the birdie sings
And nests among the trees;
The sailor sings of ropes and things
In ships upon the seas.

The children sing in far Japan,
The children sing in Spain;
The organ with the organ man
Is singing in the rain.

A GOOD PLAY

We built a ship upon the stairs
All made of the back-bedroom chairs,
And filled it full of sofa pillows
To go a-sailing on the billows.

We took a saw and several nails,
And water in the nursery pails;
And Tom said, "Let us also take
An apple and a slice of cake;"
Which was enough for Tom and me
To go a-sailing on, till tea.

We sailed along for days and days,
And had the very best of plays;
But Tom fell out and hurt his knee,
So there was no one left but me.

LOOKING FORWARD

When I am grown to man's estate
I shall be very proud and great.
And tell the other girls and boys
Not to meddle with my toys.

TRAVEL

I SHOULD like to rise and go
Where the golden apples grow;—
Where below another sky
Parrot islands anchored lie,
And, watched by cockatoos and goats,
Lonely Crusoes building boats;—
Where in sunshine reaching out
Eastern cities, miles about,
Are with mosque and minaret
Among sandy gardens set,
And the rich goods from near and far
Hang for sale in the bazaar;—
Where the Great Wall round China goes,

And on one side the desert blows,
And with bell and voice and drum,
Cities on the other hum;—
Where are forests, hot as fire,
Wide as England, tall as a spire,
Full of apes and cocoanuts
And the Negro hunters' huts;
Where the knotty crocodile
Lies and blinks in the Nile,
And the red flamingo flies
Hunting fish before his eyes;
Where in jungles, near and far,
Man-devouring tigers are,
Lying close and giving ear
Lest the hunt be drawing near,
Or a comer-by be seen
Swinging in a palanquin;
Where among the desert sands
Some deserted city stands,
All its children, sweep and prince,
Grown to manhood ages since,
Not a foot in street or house,
Not a stir of child or mouse,
And when kindly falls the night,
In all the town no spark of light.
There I'll come when I'm a man
With a camel caravan;
Light a fire in the gloom

Of some dusty dining room;
See the pictures on the walls,
Heroes, fights and festivals;
And in a corner find the toys
Of the old Egyptian boys.

WHERE GO THE BOATS?

DARK brown is the river,
  Golden is the sand.
It flows along for ever,
  With trees on either hand.

Green leaves a-floating,
  Castles of the foam,
Boats of mine a-boating—
  Where will all come home?

On goes the river
  And out past the mill,
Away down the valley,
  Away down the hill.

Away down the river,
  A hundred miles or more,
Other little children
  Shall bring my boats ashore.

AUNTIE'S SKIRTS

WHENEVER Auntie moves around,
Her dresses make a curious sound;
They trail behind her up the floor,
And trundle after through the door.

THE LAND OF COUNTERPANE

WHEN I was sick and lay abed,
I had two pillows at my head,
And all my toys beside me lay
To keep me happy all the day.

And sometimes for an hour or so
I watched my leaden soldiers go,
With different uniforms and drills,
Among the bedclothes, through the hills;

And sometimes sent my ships in fleets
All up and down among the sheets;
Or brought my trees and houses out,
And planted cities all about.

I was the giant great and still
That sits upon the pillow hill,
And sees before him, dale and plain,
The pleasant land of counterpane.

THE LAND OF NOD

From breakfast on all through the day
At home among my friends I stay;
But every night I go abroad
Afar into the land of Nod.

All by myself I have to go,
With none to tell me what to do
All alone beside the streams
And up the mountainsides of dreams.

The strangest things are there for me,
Both things to eat and things to see,
And many frightening sights abroad
Till morning in the land of Nod.

Try as I like to find the way,
I never can get back by day,
Nor can remember plain and clear
The curious music that I hear.

SYSTEM

EVERY night my prayers I say,
And get my dinner every day;
And every day that I've been good,
I get an orange after food.

The child that is not clean and neat,
With lots of toys and things to eat,
He is a naughty child, I'm sure—
Or else his dear papa is poor.

MY SHADOW

I HAVE a little shadow that goes in and out with me,
And what can be the use of him is more than I can see.
He is very, very like me from the heels up to the head;
And I see him jump before me, when I jump into my bed.

The funniest thing about him is the way he likes to grow—
Not at all like proper children, which is always very slow;
For he sometimes shoots up taller like an india-rubber
ball,
And he sometimes get so little that there's none of him
at all.

He hasn't got a notion of how children ought to play,
And can only make a fool of me in every sort of way.
He stays so close beside me, he's a coward you can see;
I'd think shame to stick to nurse as that shadow sticks
to me!

One morning, very early, before the sun was up,
I rose and found the shining dew on every buttercup;
But my lazy little shadow, like an arrant sleepyhead,
Had stayed at home behind me and was fast asleep
in bed.

A GOOD BOY

I WOKE before the morning, I was happy all the day,
I never said an ugly word, but smiled and stuck to play.

And now at last the sun is going down behind the wood,
And I am very happy, for I know that I've been good.

My bed is waiting cool and fresh, with linen smooth and
fair,
And I must off to sleepsin-by, and not forget my prayer.

I know that, till tomorrow I shall see the sun arise,
No ugly dream shall fright my mind, no ugly sight my
eyes,

But slumber hold me tightly till I waken in the dawn,
And hear the thrushes singing in the lilacs round the
lawn.

ESCAPE AT BEDTIME

THE lights from the parlour and kitchen shone out
   Through the blinds and the windows and bars;
And high overhead and all moving about,
   There were thousands of millions of stars.
There ne'er were such thousands of leaves on a tree,
   Nor of people in church or the park,
As the crowds of the stars that looked down upon me,
   And that glittered and winked in the dark.

The Dog, and the Plough, and the Hunter, and all,
  And the star of the sailor, and Mars,
These shone in the sky, and the pail by the wall,
  Would be half full of water and stars.
They saw me at last, and they chased me with cries,
  And they soon had me packed into bed;
But the glory kept shining and bright in my eyes,
  And the stars going round in my head.

MARCHING SONG

BRING the comb and play upon it!
Marching, here we come!
Willie cocks his highland bonnet,
Johnnie beats the drum.

Mary Jane commands the party,
Peter leads the rear;
Feet in time, alert and hearty,
Each a Grenadier!

All in the most martial manner
Marching double-quick;
While the napkin like a banner
Waves upon the stick!

Here's enough of fame and pillage,
Great commander Jane!
Now that we've been round the village
Let's go home again.

THE COW

THE friendly cow all red and white,
  I love with all my heart:
She gives me cream with all her might,
  To eat with apple tart.

She wanders lowing here and there,
  And yet she cannot stray,
All in the pleasant open air,
  The pleasant light of day;

And blown by all the winds that pass
  And wet with all the showers,
She walks among the meadow grass
  And eats the meadow flowers.

THE WIND

I SAW you toss the kites on high
And blow the birds about the sky;
And all around I heard you pass,
Like ladies' skirts across the grass—
    O wind, a-blowing all day long,
    O wind, that sings so loud a song!

I saw the different things you did,
But always you yourself you hid.
I felt you push, I heard you call,
I could not see yourself at all—
    O wind, a-blowing all day long,
    O wind, that sings so loud a song!

O you that are so strong and cold,
O blower, are you young or old?
Are you a beast of field and tree,
Or just a stronger child than me?
    O wind, a-blowing all day long,
    O wind, that sings so loud a song!

KEEPSAKE MILL

Over the borders, a sin without pardon,
Breaking the branches and crawling below,
Out through the breach in the wall of the garden,
Down by the banks of the river, we go.
Here is the mill with the humming of thunder,
Here is the weir with the wonder of foam,
Here is the sluice with the race running under—
Marvellous places, though handy to home!

Sounds of the village grow stiller and stiller
Stiller the note of the birds on the hill;
Dusty and dim are the eyes of the miller,
Deaf are his ears with the moil of the mill.

Years may go by, and the wheel in the river
Wheel as it wheels for us, children, today,

Wheel and keep roaring and foaming forever
Long after all of the boys are away.

Home from the Indies and home from the ocean,
Heroes and soldiers we all shall come home;
Still we shall find the old mill wheel in motion,
Turning and churning that river to foam.

You with the bean that I gave when we quarreled,
I with your marble of Saturday last,
Honoured and old and all gaily apparelled,
Here we shall meet and remember the past.

GOOD AND BAD CHILDREN

CHILDREN, you are very little,
And your bones are very brittle;
If you would grow great and stately,
You must try to walk sedately.

You must still be bright and quiet,
And content with simple diet;
And remain, through all bewild'ring,
Innocent and honest children.

Happy hearts and happy faces,
Happy play in grassy places—
That was how, in ancient ages,
Children grew to kings and sages.

But the unkind and the unruly,
And the sort who eat unduly,
They must never hope for glory—
Theirs is quite a different story!

Cruel children, crying babies,
All grow up as geese and gabies,
Hated, as their age increases,
By their nephews and their nieces.

HAPPY THOUGHT

The world is so full of a number of things,
I'm sure we should all be as happy as kings.

THE SUN'S TRAVELS

The sun is not abed, when I
At night upon my pillow lie;
Still round the earth his way he takes,
And morning after morning makes.

While here at home, in shining day,
We round the sunny garden play,
Each little Indian sleepyhead
Is being kissed and put to bed.

And when at eve I rise from tea,
Day dawns beyond the Atlantic Sea,
And all the children in the West
Are getting up and being dressed.

FOREIGN CHILDREN

LITTLE Indian, Sioux or Crow,
  Little frosty Eskimo,
  Little Turk or Japanee,
O! don't you wish that you were me?

You have seen the scarlet trees
And the lions over seas;
You have eaten ostrich eggs,
And turned the turtles off their legs.

Such a life is very fine,
But it's not so nice as mine:
You must often, as you trod,
Have wearied *not* to be abroad.

You have curious things to eat,
I am fed on proper meat;
You must dwell beyond the foam,
But I am safe and live at home.

Little Indian, Sioux or Crow,
  Little frosty Eskimo,
  Little Turk or Japanee,
O! don't you wish that you were me?

THE LAMPLIGHTER

My tea is nearly ready and the sun has left the sky;
It's time to take the window to see Leerie going by;
For every night at teatime and before you take your seat,
With lantern and with ladder he comes posting up the
street.

Now Tom would be a driver and Maria go to sea,
And my papa's a banker and as rich as he can be;
But I, when I am stronger and can choose what I'm to do,
O Leerie, I'll go round at night and light the lamps with
you!

For we are very lucky, with a lamp before the door,
And Leerie stops to light it as he lights so many more;
And O! before you hurry by with ladder and with light,
O Leerie, see a little child and nod to him tonight!

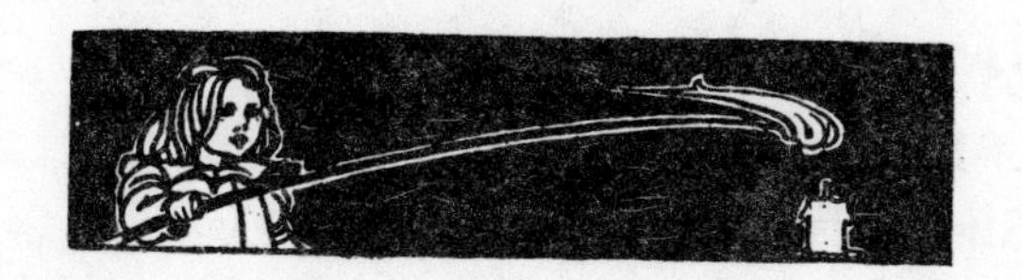

MY BED IS A BOAT

My bed is like a little boat;
   Nurse helps me in when I embark;
She girds me in my sailor's coat
   And starts me in the dark.

At night, I go on board and say
   Good night to all my friends on shore;
I shut my eyes and sail away
   And see and hear no more.

And sometimes things to bed I take,
   As prudent sailors have to do:
Perhaps a slice of wedding cake,
   Perhaps a toy or two.

All night across the dark we steer:
   But when the day returns at last
Safe in my room, beside the pier,
   I find my vessel fast.

THE MOON

THE moon has a face like the clock in the hall;
She shines on thieves on the garden wall,
On streets and fields and harbour quays,
And birdies asleep in the forks of the trees.

The squalling cat and the squeaking mouse,
The howling dog by the door of the house,
The bat that lies in bed at noon,
All love to be out by the light of the moon.

But all the things that belong to the day
Cuddle to sleep to be out of her way;
And flowers and children close their eyes
Till up in the morning the sun shall rise.

THE SWING

How do you like to go up in a swing,
Up in the air so blue?
Oh, I do think it the pleasantest thing
Ever a child can do!

Up in the air and over the wall,
Till I can see so wide,
Rivers and trees and cattle and all
Over the countryside—

Till I look down on the garden green,
Down on the roof so brown—
Up in the air I go flying again,
Up in the air and down!

TIME TO RISE

A BIRDIE with a yellow bill
Hopped upon the window sill,
Cocked his shining eye and said:
"Ain't you 'shamed, you sleepyhead?"

FAIRY BREAD

COME up here, O dusty feet!
  Here is a fairy bread to eat.
Here in my retiring room,
  Children, you may dine
On the golden smell of broom
  And the shade of pine;
And when you have eaten well,
Fairy stories hear and tell.

LOOKING-GLASS RIVER

SMOOTH it slides upon its travel
Here a wimple, there a gleam—
O the clean gravel!
O the smooth stream!

Sailing blossoms, silver fishes,
Paven pools as clear as air—
How a child wishes
To live down there!

We can see our coloured faces
Floating on the shaken pool
Down in cool places,
Dim and very cool;

Till a wind or water wrinkle,
Dipping marten, plumping trout,
Spreads in a twinkle
And blots all out.

See the rings pursue each other;
All below grows black as night
Just as if mother
Had blown out the light!

Patience, children, just a minute—
See the spreading circles die;
The stream and all in it
Will clear by-and-by.

FROM A RAILWAY CARRIAGE

FASTER than fairies, faster than witches,
Bridges and houses, hedges and ditches;
And charging along like troops in a battle,
All through the meadows the horses and cattle;
All of the sights of the hill and the plain
Fly as thick as driving rain;
And ever again, in the wink of an eye,
Painted stations whistle by.

Here is a child who clambers and scrambles,
All by himself and gathering brambles;
Here is a tramp who stands and gazes;
And there is the green for stringing the daisies!
Here is a cart run away in the road
Lumping along with man and load;
And here is a mill and there is a river;
Each a glimpse and gone for ever!

WINTERTIME

LATE lies the wintry sun abed,
A frosty, fiery sleepyhead;
Blinks but an hour or two; and then,
A blood-red orange, sets again.

Before the stars have left the skies,
At morning in the dark I rise;
And shivering in my nakedness,
By the cold candle, bathe and dress.

Close by the jolly fire I sit
To warm my frozen bones a bit;
Or with a reindeer sled, explore
The colder countries round the door.

When to go out, my nurse doth wrap
Me in my comforter and cap:
The cold wind burns my face, and blows
Its frosty pepper up my nose.

Black are my steps on silver sod;
Thick blows my frosty breath abroad;
And tree and house, and hill and lake,
Are frosted like a wedding cake.

THE HAYLOFT

THROUGH all the pleasant meadowside
The grass grew shoulder-high,
Till the shining scythes went far and wide
And cut it down to dry.

These green and sweetly smelling crops
They led in wagons home;
And they piled them here in mountain tops
For mountaineers to roam.

Here is Mount Clear, Mount Rusty-Nail,
Mount Eagle and Mount High;—
The mice that in these mountains dwell,
No happier are than I!

O what a joy to clamber there,
O what a place for play,
With the sweet, the dim, the dusty air,
The happy hills of hay.

FAREWELL TO THE FARM

The coach is at the door at last;
The eager children, mounting fast
And kissing hands, in chorus sing:
Good-bye, good-bye, to everything!

To house and garden, field and lawn,
The meadow gates we swung upon,
To pump and stable, tree and swing,
Good-bye, good-bye, to everything!

And fare you well for evermore,
O ladder at the hayloft door,
O hayloft where the cobwebs cling,
Good-bye, good-bye, to everything!

Crack goes the whip, and off we go;
The trees and houses smaller grow;
Last, round the woody turn we swing:
Good-bye, good-bye, to everything!

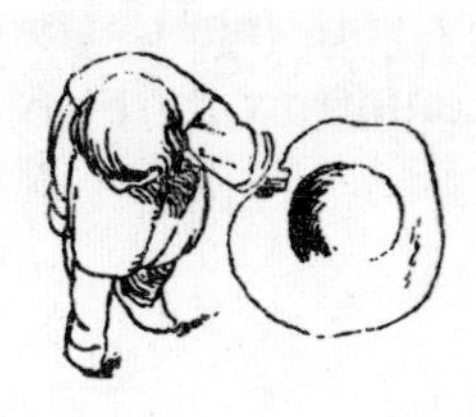

NORTHWEST PASSAGE

1. GOOD NIGHT

WHEN the bright lamp is carried in,
The sunless hours again begin;
O'er all without, in field and lane,
The haunted night returns again.

Now we behold the embers flee
About the firelit hearth; and see
Our faces painted as we pass,
Like pictures, on the window glass.

Must we to bed indeed? Well then,
Let us arise and go like men,
And face with an undaunted tread
The long black passage up to bed.

Farewell, O brother, sister, sire!
O pleasant party round the fire!
The songs you sing, the tales you tell,
Till far tomorrow, fare ye well!

2. SHADOW MARCH

All round the house is the jet-black night;
  It stares through the windowpane;
It crawls in the corners, hiding from the light,
  And it moves with the moving flame.

Now my little heart goes a-beating like a drum,
  With the breath of the Bogie in my hair;
And all round the candle the crooked shadows come
  And go marching along up the stair.

The shadow of the balusters, the shadow of the lamp,
  The shadow of the child that goes to bed—
All the wicked shadows coming tramp, tramp, tramp,
  With the black night overhead.

3. IN PORT

Last, to the chamber where I lie,
My fearful footsteps patter nigh,
And come from out the cold and gloom
Into my warm and cheerful room.

There, safe arrived, we turn about
To keep the coming shadows out,
And close the happy door at last
On all the perils that we past.

Then, when mamma goes by to bed,
She shall come in with tip-toe tread,
And see me lying warm and fast
And in the Land of Nod at last.

THE CHILD ALONE

THE UNSEEN PLAYMATE

When children are playing alone on the green,
In comes the playmate that never was seen.
When children are happy and lonely and good,
The Friend of the Children comes out of the wood.

Nobody heard him and nobody saw,
His is a picture you never could draw,
But he's sure to be present, abroad or at home,
When children are happy and playing alone.

He lies in the laurels, he runs on the grass,
He sings when you tinkle the musical glass;
Whene'er you are happy and cannot tell why,
The Friend of the Children is sure to be by!

He loves to be little, he hates to be big,
'Tis he that inhabits the caves that you dig;
'Tis he when you play with your soldiers of tin
That sides with the Frenchmen and never can win.

'Tis he, when at night you go off to your bed,
Bids you go to your sleep and not trouble your head;
For wherever they're lying, in cupboard or shelf,
'Tis he will take care of your playthings himself!

BLOCK CITY

WHAT are you able to build with your blocks?
Castles and palaces, temples and docks.
Rain may keep raining, and others go roam,
But I can be happy and building at home.

Let the sofa be mountains, the carpet be sea,
There I'll establish a city for me:
A kirk and a mill and a palace beside,
And a harbour as well where my vessels may ride.

Great is the palace with pillar and wall,
A sort of a tower on the top of it all,
And steps coming down in an orderly way
To where my toy vessels lie safe in the bay.

This one is sailing and that one is moored:
Hark to the song of the sailors on board!
And see on the steps of my palace, the kings
Coming and going with presents and things!

Now I have done with it, down let it go!
All in a moment the town is laid low.
Block upon block lying scattered and free,
What is there left of my town by the sea?

Yet as I saw it, I see it again,
The kirk and the palace, the ships and the men,
And as long as I live and where'er I may be,
I'll always remember my town by the sea.

MY SHIP AND I

O IT'S I that am the captain of a tidy little ship,
Of a ship that goes a-sailing on the pond;
And my ship it keeps a-turning all around and all about;
But when I'm a little older, I shall find the secret out
How to send my vessel sailing on beyond.

For I mean to grow as little as the dolly at the helm,
And the dolly I intend to come alive;
And with him beside to help me, it's a-sailing I shall go,
It's a-sailing on the water, when the jolly breezes blow
And the vessel goes a divie-divie-dive.

O it's then you'll see me sailing through the rushes and the reeds,
And you'll hear the water singing at the prow;
For beside the dolly sailor, I'm to voyage and explore,
To land upon the island where no dolly was before,
And to fire the penny cannon in the bow.

MY KINGDOM

Down by a shining water well
I found a very little dell,
No higher than my head.
The heather and the gorse about
In summer bloom were coming out,
Some yellow and some red.

I called the little pool a sea;
The little hills were big to me;
For I am very small.
I made a boat, I made a town,
I searched the caverns up and down,
And named them one and all.

And all about was mine, I said,
The little sparrows overhead,
The little minnows too.
This was the world and I was king;
For me the bees came by to sing,
For me the swallows flew.

I played there were no deeper seas,
Nor any wider plains than these,
    Nor other kings than me.
At last I heard my mother call
Out from the house at evenfall,
    To call me home to tea.

And I must rise and leave my dell,
And leave my dimpled water well,
    And leave my heather blooms.
Alas! and as my home I neared,
How very big my nurse appeared,
    How great and cool the rooms!

PICTURE BOOKS IN WINTER

SUMMER fading, winter comes—
Frosty mornings, tingling thumbs,
Window robins, winter rooks.
And the picture story books.

Water now is turned to stone
Nurse and I can walk upon;
Still we find the flowing brooks
In the picture story books.

All the pretty things put by,
Wait upon the children's eye,
Sheep and shepherds, trees and crooks,
In the picture story books.

We may see how all things are,
Seas and cities, near and far,
And the flying fairies' looks,
In the picture story books.

How am I to sing your praise,
Happy chimney-corner days,
Sitting safe in nursery nooks,
Reading picture story books?

MY TREASURES

THESE nuts, that I keep in the back of the nest
Where all my lead soldiers are lying at rest,
Were gathered in autumn by nursie and me
In a wood with a well by the side of the sea.

This whistle we made (and how clearly it sounds!)
By the side of a field at the end of the grounds.
Of a branch of a plane, with a knife of my own,
It was nursie who made it, and nursie alone!

The stone, with the white and the yellow and grey,
We discovered I cannot tell *how* far away;
And I carried it back although weary and cold,
For though father denies it, I'm sure it is gold.

But of all of my treasures the last is the king,
For there's very few children possess such a thing;
And that is a chisel, both handle and blade,
Which a man who was really a carpenter made.

THE LAND OF STORY BOOKS

At evening when the lamp is lit,
Around the fire my parents sit;
They sit at home and talk and sing,
And do not play at anything.

Now, with my little gun, I crawl
All in the dark along the wall,
And follow round the forest track
Away behind the sofa back.

There, in the night, when none can spy,
All in my hunter's camp I lie,
And play at books that I have read
Till it is time to go to bed.

These are the hills, these are the woods,
These are my starry solitudes;
And there the river by whose brink
The roaring lions come to drink.

I see the others far away
As if in firelit camp they lay,
And I, like an Indian scout,
Around their party prowled about.

So, when my nurse comes in for me,
Home I return across the sea,
And go to bed with backward looks
At my dear land of Story Books.

ARMIES IN THE FIRE

The lamps now glitter down the street;
Faintly sound the falling feet.
And the blue even slowly falls
About the garden trees and walls.

Now in the falling of the gloom
The red fire paints the empty room:
And warmly on the roof it looks,
And flickers on the backs of books.

Armies march by tower and spire
Of cities blazing, in the fire;—
Till as I gaze with staring eyes,
The armies fade, the lustre dies.

Then once again the glow returns;
Again the phantom city burns;
And down the red-hot valley, lo!
The phantom armies marching go!

Blinking embers, tell me true
Where are those armies marching to,
And what the burning city is
That crumbles in your furnaces?

THE LITTLE LAND

When at home alone I sit
And am very tired of it,
I have just to shut my eyes
To go sailing through the skies—
To go sailing far away
To the pleasant Land of Play;
To the fairy land afar
Where the Little People are;
Where the clover-tops are trees,
And the rain pools are the seas,
And the leaves like little ships
Sail about on tiny trips;
And above the daisy tree
    Through the grasses,
High o'erhead the Bumble Bee
    Hums and passes.

In that forest to and fro
I can wander, I can go;
See the spider and the fly,
And the ants go marching by
Carrying parcels with their feet
Down the green and grassy street.
I can in the sorrel sit
Where the ladybird alit.
I can climb the jointed grass;
        And on high
See the greater swallows pass
        In the sky,
And the round sun rolling by
Heeding no such things as I.

Through that forest I can pass
Till, as in a looking glass,
Humming fly and daisy tree

And my tiny self I see,
Painted very clear and neat
On the rain pool at my feet.
Should a leaflet come to land
Drifting near to where I stand,
Straight I'll board that tiny boat
Round the rain-pool sea to float.

Little thoughtful creatures sit
On the grassy coasts of it;
Little things with lovely eyes
See me sailing with surprise.
Some are clad in armour green—
(These have sure to battle been!)—
Some are pied with ev'ry hue,
Black and crimson, gold and blue;
Some have wings and swift are gone;—
But they all look kindly on.

When my eyes I once again
Open, and see all things plain;
High bare walls, great bare floor;
Great big knobs on drawer and door;
Great big people perched on chairs,
Stitching tucks and mending tears,
Each a hill that I could climb,
And talking nonsense all the time—

O dear me,
That I could be

A sailor on the rain-pool sea,
A climber in the clover tree,
And just come back, a sleepyhead,
Late at night to go to bed.

GARDEN DAYS

NIGHT AND DAY

When the golden day is done,
  Through the closing portal,
Child and garden, flower and sun,
  Vanish all things mortal.

As the blinding shadows fall,
  As the rays diminish,
Under evening's cloak, they all
  Roll away and vanish.

Garden darkened, daisy shut,
  Child in bed, they slumber—
Glowworm in the highway rut,
  Mice among the lumber.

In the darkness houses shine,
  Parents move with candles;
Till on all, the night divine
  Turns the bedroom handles.

Till at last the day begins
  In the east a-breaking,
In the hedges and the whins
  Sleeping birds a-waking.

In the darkness shapes of things,
  Houses, trees and hedges,
Clearer grow; and sparrow's wings
  Beat on window ledges.

These shall wake the yawning maid;
  She the door shall open—
Finding dew on garden glade
  And the morning broken.

There my garden grows again
  Green and rosy painted,
As at eve behind the pane
  From my eyes it fainted.

Just as it was shut away,
  Toylike, in the even,
Here I see it glow with day
  Under glowing heaven.

Every path and every plot,
   Every bush of roses,
Every blue forget-me-not
   Where the dew reposes,

"Up!" they cry, "the day is come
   On the smiling valleys;
We have beat the morning drum;
   Playmate, join your allies!"

BIRDS all the sunny day
  Flutter and quarrel
Here in the arbour-like
  Tent of the laurel.

Here in the fork
  The brown nest is seated;
Four little blue eggs
  The mother keeps heated.

While we stand watching her,
  Staring like gabies,
Safe in each egg are the
  Bird's little babies.

Soon the frail eggs they shall
  Chip, and upspringing
Make all the April woods
  Merry with singing.

Younger than we are,
  O children, and frailer,
Soon in blue air they'll be,
  Singer and sailor.

We, so much older,
  Taller and stronger,
We shall look down on the
  Birdies no longer.

They shall go flying
   With musical speeches
High overhead in the
   Tops of the beeches.

In spite of our wisdom
   And sensible talking,
We on our feet must go
   Plodding and walking.

THE FLOWERS

ALL the names I know from nurse:
Gardener's garters, Shepherd's purse,
Bachelor's buttons, Lady's smock,
And the Lady Hollyhock.

Fairy places, fairy things,
Fairy woods where the wild bee wings,
Tiny trees for tiny dames—
These must all be fairy names!

Tiny woods below whose boughs
Shady fairies weave a house;
Tiny treetops, rose or thyme,
Where the braver fairies climb!

Fair are grown-up people's trees,
But the fairest woods are these;
Where if I were not so tall,
I should live for good and all.

SUMMER SUN

GREAT is the sun, and wide he goes
Through empty heaven without repose;
And in the blue and glowing days
More thick than rain he showers his rays.

Though closer still the blinds we pull
To keep the shady parlour cool,
Yet he will find a chink or two
To slip his golden fingers through.

The dusty attic spider-clad
He, through the keyhole, maketh glad;
And through the broken edge of tiles,
Into the laddered hayloft smiles.

Meantime his golden face around
He bares to all the garden ground,
And sheds a warm and glittering look
Among the ivy's inmost nook.

Above the hills, along the blue,
Round the bright air with footing true,
To please the child, to paint the rose,
The gardener of the World, he goes.

THE DUMB SOLDIER

WHEN the grass was closely mown,
Walking on the lawn alone,
In the turf a hole I found
And hid a soldier underground.

Spring and daisies came apace;
Grasses hide my hiding place;
Grasses run like a green sea
O'er the lawn up to my knee.

Under grass alone he lies,
Looking up with leaden eyes,
Scarlet coat and pointed gun,
To the stars and to the sun.

When the grass is ripe like grain,
When the scythe is stoned again,
When the lawn is shaven clear,
Then my hole shall reappear.

I shall find him, never fear,
I shall find my grenadier;
But for all that's gone and come,
I shall find my soldier dumb.

He has lived, a little thing,
In the grassy woods of spring;
Done, if he could tell me true,
Just as I should like to do.

He has seen the starry hours
And the springing of the flowers;
And the fairy things that pass
In the forests of the grass.

In the silence he has heard
Talking bee and ladybird,
And the butterfly has flown
O'er him as he lay alone.

Not a word will he disclose,
Not a word of all he knows;
I must lay him on the shelf,
And make up the tale myself.

THE GARDENER

THE gardener does not love to talk,
He makes me keep the gravel walk;
And when he puts his tools away,
He locks the door and takes the key.

Away behind the currant row
Where no one else but cook may go,
Far in the plots, I see him dig,
Old and serious, brown and big.

He digs the flowers, green, red, and blue,
Nor wishes to be spoken to.
He digs the flowers and cuts the hay,
And never seems to want to play.

Silly gardener! summer goes,
And winter comes with pinching toes,
When in the garden bare and brown
You must lay your barrow down.

Well now, and while the summer stays,
To profit by these garden days,
O how much wiser you would be
To play at Indian wars with me!

AUTUMN FIRES

In the other gardens
  And all up the vale,
From the autumn bonfires
  See the smoke trail!

Pleasant summer over
  And all the summer flowers,
The red fire blazes,
  The grey smoke towers.

Sing a song of seasons!
  Something bright in all!
Flowers in the summer,
  Fires in the fall!

HISTORICAL ASSOCIATIONS

Dear Uncle Jim, this garden ground
That now you smoke your pipe around,
Has seen immortal actions done
And valiant battles lost and won.

Here we had best on tip-toe tread,
While I for safety march ahead,
For this is that enchanted ground
Where all who loiter slumber sound.

Here is the sea, here is the sand,
Here is simple Shepherd's Land,
Here are the fairy hollyhocks,
And there are Ali Baba's rocks.

But yonder, see! apart and high,
Frozen Siberia lies; where I,
With Robert Bruce and William Tell,
Was bound by an enchanter's spell.

There, then, awhile in chains we lay,
In wintry dungeons, far from day;
But ris'n at length, with might and main,
Our iron fetters burst in twain.

Then all the horns were blown in town;
And to the ramparts clanging down,
All the giants leaped to horse
And charged behind us through the gorse.

On we rode, the others and I,
Over the mountains blue, and by
The Silver River, the sounding sea,
And the robber woods of Tartary.

A thousand miles we galloped fast,
And down the witches' lane we passed,
And rode amain, with brandished sword,
Up to the middle, through the ford.

Last we drew rein—a weary three—
Upon the lawn, in time for tea,
And from our steeds alighted down
Before the gates of Babylon.

ENVOYS

TO WILLIE AND HENRIETTA

If two may read aright
These rhymes of old delight
And house and garden play,
You two, my cousins, and you only, may.

You in a garden green
With me were king and queen,
Were hunter, soldier, tar,
And all the thousand things that children are.

Now in the elder's seat
We rest with quiet feet,
And from the window bay
We watch the children, our successors, play.

"Time was," the golden head
Irrevocably said;
But time which none can bind,
While flowing fast away, leaves love behind.

TO MY MOTHER

You too, my mother, read my rhymes
For love of unforgotten times,
And you may chance to hear once more
The little feet along the floor.

TO AUNTIE

CHIEF *of our aunts*—not only I,
But all your dozen of nurslings cry—
What did the other children do?
And what were childhood, wanting you?

TO MINNIE

The red room with the giant bed
Where none but elders laid their head;
The little room where you and I
Did for awhile together lie
And, simple suitor, I your hand
In decent marriage did demand;
The great day nursery, best of all,
With pictures pasted on the wall
And leaves upon the blind—
A pleasant room wherein to wake
And hear the leafy garden shake
And rustle in the wind—
And pleasant there to lie in bed
And see the pictures overhead—
The wars about Sebastopol,
The grinning guns along the wall,
The daring escalade,
The plunging ships, the bleating sheep,

The happy children ankle-deep
And laughing as they wade:

All these are vanished clean away,
And the old manse is changed today;
It wears an altered face
And shields a stranger race.
The river, on from mill to mill,
Flows past our childhood's garden still;
But ah! we children never more
Shall watch it from the water door!
Below the yew—it still is there—
Our phantom voices haunt the air
As we were still at play,
And I can hear them call and say:
"How far is it to Babylon?"

Ah, far enough, my dear,
Far, far enough from here—
Yet you have farther gone!

"Can I get there by candlelight?"
So goes the old refrain.
I do not know—perchance you might—
But only, children, hear it right,
Ah, never to return again!
The eternal dawn, beyond a doubt,
Shall break on hill and plain,
And put all stars and candles out,
Ere we be young again.

To you in distant India, these
I send across the seas,
Nor count it far across.
For which of us forgets
The Indian cabinets,
The bones of antelope, the wings of albatross,
The pied and painted birds and beans,
The junks and bangles, beads and screens,
The gods and sacred bells,
And the loud-humming, twisted shells?
The level of the parlour floor
Was honest, homely, Scottish shore;
But when we climbed upon a chair,
Behold the gorgeous East was there!
Be this a fable; and behold
Me in the parlour as of old,
And Minnie just above me set
In the quaint Indian cabinet!

Smiling and kind, you grace a shelf
Too high for me to reach myself.
Reach down a hand, my dear, and take
These rhymes for old acquaintance' sake.

TO MY NAME-CHILD

I

Some day soon this rhyming volume, if you learn with proper speed,
Little Louis Sanchez, will be given you to read.
Then shall you discover, that your name was printed down
By the English printers, long before, in London town.

In the great and busy city where the East and West are met,
All the little letters did the English printer set;
While you thought of nothing, and were still too young to play,
Foreign people thought of you in places far away.

Ay, and while you slept, a baby, over all the English
lands
Other little children took the volume in their hands;
Other children questioned, in their homes across the seas:
Who was little Louis, won't you tell us, mother, please?

II

Now that you have spelt your lesson, lay it down and go
and play,
Seeking shells and seaweed on the sands of Monterey,
Watching all the mighty whalebones, lying buried by the
breeze,
Tiny sandy-pipers, and the huge Pacific seas.

And remember in your playing, as the seafog rolls to you,
Long ere you could read it, how I told you what to do;
And that while you thought of no one, nearly half the
world away
Some one thought of Louis on the beach of Monterey!

TO ANY READER

As from the house your mother sees
You playing round the garden trees
So you may see, if you will look
Through the windows of this book,
Another child, far, far away,
And in another garden, play.
But do not think you can at all,
By knocking on the window, call
That child to hear you. He intent
Is all on his play business bent.
He does not hear; he will not look,
Nor yet be lured out of this book.
For, long ago, the truth to say,
He has grown up and gone away,
And it is but a child of air
That lingers in the garden there.

PART II

UNDER
THE
WIDE
AND
STARRY
SKY

CONTENTS

UNDER THE WIDE AND STARRY SKY

REQUIEM

UNDER the wide and starry sky,
    Dig the grave and let me lie.
Glad did I live and gladly die,
    And I laid me down with a will.

This be the verse you grave for me:
Here he lies where he longed to be;
Home is the sailor, home from sea,
    And the hunter home from the hill.

IN THE STATES

With half a heart I wander here
    As from an age gone by
A brother—yet though young in years,
    An elder brother, I.

You speak another tongue than mine,
    Though both were English born.
I towards the night of time decline
    You mount into the morn.

Youth shall grow great and strong and free,
    But age must still decay:
Tomorrow for the States—for me,
    England and Yesterday.

San Francisco

THE VAGABOND

(To an air of Schubert)

GIVE to me the life I love,
    Let the lave go by me,
Give the jolly heaven above
    And the byway nigh me.
Bed in the bush with stars to see,
    Bread I dip in the river–
There's the life for a man like me,
    There's the life forever.

Let the blow fall soon or late,
    Let what will be o'er me;
Give the face of earth around,
    And the road before me.
Wealth I seek not, hope nor love,
    Nor a friend to know me;
All I seek is the heaven above
    And the road below me.

Or let autumn fall on me
    Where afield I linger,
Silencing the bird on tree,
    Biting the blue finger.

White as meal the frosty field—
    Warm the fireside haven—
Not to autumn will I yield,
    Nor to winter even!

Let the blow fall soon or late,
    Let what will be o'er me;
Give the face of earth around,
    And the road before me.
Wealth I ask not, hope nor love,
    Nor a friend to know me.
All I ask is heaven above,
    And the road below me.

YOUTH AND LOVE—I

ONCE only by the garden gate
Our lips we joined and parted
I must fulfill an empty fate
And travel the uncharted.

Hail and farewell! I must arise,
Leave here the fatted cattle,
And paint on foreign lands and skies
My Odyssey of battle.

The untented Kosmos my abode,
I pass, a wilful stranger:
My mistress still the open road
And the bright eyes of danger.

Come ill or well, the cross, the crown,
The rainbow or the thunder,
I fling my soul and body down
For God to plough them under.

YOUTH AND LOVE—II

To the heart of youth the world is a highwayside
Passing forever, he fares; and on either hand.
Deep in the gardens golden pavilions hide,
Nestle in orchard bloom, and far on the level land
Call him with lighted lamp in the eventide.

Thick as the stars at night when the moon is down,
Pleasures assail him. He to his nobler fate
Fares; and but waves a hand as he passes on,
Cries but a wayside word to her at the garden gate,
Sings but a boyish stave and his face is gone.

THE UNFORGOTTEN—I

In dreams, unhappy, I behold you stand
As heretofore;
The unremembered tokens in your hand
Avail no more.

No more the morning glow, no more the grace,
Enshrines, endears.
Cold beats the light of time upon your face
And shows your tears.

He came, he went. Perchance you wept a while
And then forgot.
Ah me! but he that left you with a smile
Forgets you not.

THE UNFORGOTTEN—II

She rested by the Broken Brook
She drank of Weary Well.
She moved beyond my lingering look,
Ah, whither none can tell!

She came, she went. In other lands,
Perchance in fairer skies,
Her hands shall cling with other hands,
Her eyes to other eyes.

She vanished. In the sounding town
Will she remember, too?
Will she recall the eyes of brown
As I recall the blue?

THE INFINITE SHINING HEAVENS

THE infinite shining heavens
Rose and I saw in the night
Uncountable angel stars
Showering sorrow and light.

I saw them distant as heaven,
Dumb and shining and dead,
And the idle stars of the night
Were dearer to me than bread.

Night after night in my sorrow
The stars stood over the sea,
Till lo! I looked in the dusk
And a star had come down to me.

THE STORMY EVENING

THE stormy evening closes now in vain,
Loud wails the wind and beats the driving rain,
While here in sheltered house
With fire-painted walls,
I hear the wind abroad,
I hark the calling squalls—
"Blow, blow," I cry, "you burst your cheeks in vain!
Blow, blow," I cry, "my love is home again!"

Yon ship you chase perchance but yesternight
Bore still the precious freight of my delight,
That here in sheltered house
With fire-painted walls,
Now hears the wind abroad,
Now harks the calling squalls.
"Blow, blow," I cry, "in vain you rouse the sea,
My rescued sailor shares the fire with me!"

TO AN ISLAND PRINCESS

SINCE long ago, a child at home,
I read and longed to rise and roam.
Where'er I went, whate'er I willed,
One promised land my fancy filled.
Hence the long roads my home I made;
Tossed much in ships: have often laid
Below the uncurtained sky my head,
Rain-deluged and wind-buffeted.
And many a thousand hills I crossed
And corners turned—Love's labour lost,
Till, Lady, to your isle of sun
I came, not hoping; and, like one
Snatched out of blindness, rubbed my eyes,
And hailed my promised land with cries.

Yes, Lady, here I was at last;
Here found I all I had forecast:
The long roll of the sapphire sea
That keeps the land's virginity;
The stalwart giants of the wood

Laden with toys and flowers and food;
The precious forest pouring out
To compass the whole town about:
The town itself with streets of lawn,
Loved of the moon, blessed by the dawn,
Where the brown children all the day
Keep up a ceaseless noise of play,

Play in the sun, play in the rain,
Not ever quarrel or complain.
And late at night, in the woods of fruit,
Hark! do you hear the passing flute?

I threw one look to either hand,
And knew I was in Fairyland.
And yet one point of being so,
I lacked. For, Lady (as you know),
Whoever by his might of hand
Won entrance into Fairyland,
Found always with admiring eyes
A Fairy princess kind and wise.

It was not long I waited; soon
Upon my threshold, in broad noon,
Fair and helpful, wise and good,
The Fairy Princess Moë stood.

TANTIRA, TAHITI, 1888

IN MEMORIAM F. A. S.

Yet, O stricken heart, remember, O remember
How of human days he lived the better part.
April came to bloom and never dim December
Breathed its killing chills upon the head or heart.

Doomed to know not Winter, only Spring, a being
Trod the flowery April blithely for awhile,
Took his fill of music, joy of thought and seeing,
Came and stayed and went, nor ever ceased to smile.

Came and stayed and went, and now when all is finished,
You alone have crossed the melancholy stream,
Yours the pang, but his, O his, the undiminished
Undecaying gladness, undeparted dream.

All that life contains of torture, toil, and treason,
Shame, dishonour, death, to him were but a name.
Here, a boy, he dwelt through all the singing season
And ere the day of sorrow departed as he came.

Davos, 1881

I WILL MAKE YOU BROOCHES

I WILL make you brooches and toys for your delight
Of bird-song at morning and star-shine at night.
I will make a palace fit for you and me
Of green days in forests and blue days at sea.

I will make my kitchen, and you shall keep your room,
Where white flows the river and bright blows the broom,
And you shall wash your linen and keep your body white
In rainfall at morning and dewfall at night.

And this shall be for music when no one else is near,
The fine song for singing, the rare song to hear!
That only I remember, that only you admire,
Of the broad road that stretches and the roadside fire.

MADRIGAL

PLAIN as the glistering planets shine
When winds have cleaned the skies,
Her love appeared, appealed for mine
And wantoned in her eyes.

Clear as the shining tapers burned
On Cytherea's shrine,
Those brimming lustrous beauties turned,
And called and conquered mine.

The beacon-lamp that Hero lit
No fairer shone on sea,
No plainlier summoned will and wit,
Than hers encouraged me.

I thrilled to feel her influence near,
I struck my flag at sight.
Her starry silence smote my ear
Like sudden drums at night.

I ran as, at the cannon's roar,
The troops the ramparts man—
As in the holy house of yore
The willing Eli ran.

Here, lady, lo! that servant stands
    You picked from passing men,
And should you need nor heart nor hands
    He bows and goes again.

TO YOU, LET SNOW AND ROSES

To you, let snow and roses
    And golden locks belong.
These are the world's enslavers,
    Let these delight the throng.
For her of duskier lustre
    Whose favour still I wear,
The snow be in her kirtle,
    The rose be in her hair!

The hue of highland rivers
    Careering, full and cool,
From sable on to golden,
    From rapid on to pool—
The hue of heather-honey,
    The hue of honey-bees,
Shall tinge her golden shoulder,
    Shall gild her tawny knees.

WE HAVE LOVED OF YORE

(To an air of Diabelli)

BERRIED brake and reedy island,
Heaven below, and only heaven above,
Through the sky's inverted azure
Softly swam the boat that bore our love.
Bright were your eyes as the day;
Bright ran the stream,
Bright hung the sky above.
Days of April, airs of Eden,
How the glory died through golden hours,
And the shining moon arising
How the boat drew homeward filled with flowers!
Bright were your eyes in the night:
We have lived, my love—
O, we have loved, my love.

Frost has bound our flowing river,
    Snow has whitened all our island brake,
And beside the winter fagot
    Joan and Darby doze and dream and wake.
        Still, in the river of dreams
        Swims the boat of love—
        Hark! chimes the falling oar!
And again in winter evenings
    When on firelight dreaming fancy feeds,
In whose ears of aged lovers
    Love's own river warbles in the reeds.
        Love still the past, O, my love!
        We have lived of yore,
        O, we have loved of yore.

MATER TRIUMPHANS

Son of my woman's body, you go, to the drum and fife,
To taste the colour of love and the other side of life—
From out of the dainty the rude, the strong from out of the frail,
Eternally through the ages from the female comes the male.

The ten fingers and toes, and the shell-like nail on each,
The eyes blind as gems and the tongue attempting speech;
Impotent hands in my bosom, and yet they shall wield the sword!
Drugged with slumber and milk, you wait the day of the Lord.

Infant bridegroom, uncrowned king, unanointed priest,
Soldier, lover, explorer, I see you nozzle the breast.
You that grope in my bosom shall load the ladies with rings,
You, that came forth through the doors, shall burst the doors of Kings.

BRIGHT IS THE RING OF WORDS

Bright is the ring of words
    When the right man rings them,
Fair the fall of songs
    When the singer sings them.
Still they are carolled and said—
    On wings they are carried—
After the singer is dead
    And the maker buried.

Low as the singer lies
    In the field of heather,
Songs of his fashion bring
    The swains together.
And when the west is red
    With the sunset embers,
The lover lingers and sings
    And the maid remembers.

IN THE HIGHLANDS

In the highlands, in the country places,
Where the old plain men have rosy faces,
And the young fair maidens
Quiet eyes;
Where essential silence cheers and blesses,
And forever in the hill-recesses
Her more lovely music
Broods and dies.

O to mount again where once I haunted;
Where the old red hills are bird-enchanted,
And the low green meadows
Bright with sward;
And when evening dies, the million-tinted,
And the night has come, and planets glinted,
Lo! the valley hollow,
Lamp-bestarred.

O to dream, O to awake and wander
There, and with delight to take and render,
Through the trance of silence,
Quiet breath;
Lo! for there, among the flowers and grasses,
Only the mightier movement sounds and passes,
Only winds and rivers,
Life and death.

TO DR. HAKE

(On receiving a copy of verses)

In the beloved hour that ushers day,
In the pure dew, under the breaking grey,
One bird, ere yet the woodland quires awake,
With brief reveillé summons all the brake:
Chirp, chirp, it goes; nor waits an answer long;
And that small signal fills the grove with song.

Thus on my pipe I breathed a strain or two;
It scarce was music, but 'twas all I knew.
It was not music, for I lacked the art,
Yet what but frozen music filled my heart?
Chirp, chirp, I went, nor hoped a nobler strain;
But Heaven decreed I should not pipe in vain,
For, lo! not far from there, in secret dale,
All silent, sat an ancient nightingale.
My sparrow notes he heard; thereat awoke;
And with a tide of song his silence broke.

WANDERING WILLIE

Home no more home to me, whither must I wander?
    Hunger my driver, I go where I must,
Cold blows the winter wind over hill and heather;
    Thick drives the rain, and my roof is in the dust.
Loved of wise men was the shade of my roof-tree.
    The true word of welcome was spoken in the door—
Dear days of old, with the faces in the firelight,
    Kind folks of old, you come again no more.

Home was home then, my dear, full of kindly faces,
    Home was home then, my dear, happy for the child.
Fire and the windows bright glittered on the moorland;
    Song, tuneful song, built a palace in the wild.
Now, when day dawns on the brow of the moorland,

Lone stands the house, and the chimney-stone is cold.
Lone let it stand, now the friends are all departed,
The kind hearts, the true hearts, that loved the place of old.

Spring shall come, come again, calling up the moor-fowl,
Spring shall bring the sun and rain, bring the bees and flowers;
Red shall the heather bloom over hill and valley,
Soft flow the stream through the even-flowing hours;
Fair the day shine as it shone on my childhood
Fair shine the day on the house with open door;
Birds come and cry there and twitter in the chimney—
But I go forever and come again no more.

TO—

I KNEW thee strong and quiet like the hills;
I knew thee apt to pity, brave to endure:
In peace or war a Roman full equipped.
And just I knew thee, like the fabled kings
Who by the loud sea-shore gave judgment forth,
From dawn to eve, bearded and few of words.
What, what, was I to honour thee? A child,
A youth in ardour but a child in strength,
Who after virtue's golden chariot wheels
Runs ever panting, nor attains the goal.
So thought I, and was sorrowful at heart.

Since then my steps have visited that flood
Along whose shore the numerous footfalls cease,
The voices and the tears of life expire.
Thither the prints go down, the hero's way
Trod large upon the sand, the trembling maid's;
Nimrod that wound his trumpet in the wood,
And the poor, dreaming child, hunter of flowers,
That here his hunting closes with the great.
So one and all go down, nor aught returns.

For thee, for us, the sacred river waits;
For me, the unworthy; thee, the perfect friend.
There Blame desists, there his unfaltering dogs
He from the chase recalls, and homeward rides;

Yet Praise and Love pass over and go in.
So when, beside that margin, I discard
My more than mortal weakness, and with thee
Through that still land unfearing I advance:
If then at all we keep the touch of joy
Thou shalt rejoice to find me altered—I,
O Felix, to behold thee still unchanged.

THE MORNING DRUM-CALL

THE morning drum-call on my eager ear
Thrills unforgotten yet; the morning dew
    Lies yet undried along my field of noon.
But now I pause at whiles in what I do,
And count the bell, and tremble lest I hear
    (My work untrimmed) the sunset gun too soon.

I HAVE TROD

I HAVE trod the upward and the downward slope;
I have endured and done in days before;
I have longed for all, and bid farewell to hope;
And I have lived and loved, and closed the door.

HE HEARS WITH GLADDENED HEART

He hears with gladdened heart the thunder
    Peal, and loves the falling dew;
He knows the earth above and under—
    Sits and is content to view.

He sits beside the dying ember,
    God for hope and man for friend,
Content to see, glad to remember,
    Expectant of the certain end.

THE LOST OCCASION

FAREWELL, fair day and fading light!
The clay-born here, with westward sight,
Marks the huge sun now downward soar.
Farewell. We twain shall meet no more.

Farewell. I watch with bursting sigh
My late contemned occasion die.
I linger useless in my tent:
Farewell, fair day, so foully spent!

Farewell, fair day. If any God
At all consider this poor clod,
He who the fair occasion sent
Prepared and placed the impediment.

Let him diviner vengeance take—
Give me to sleep, give me to wake
Girded and shod, and bid me play
The hero in the coming day!

WINTER

In rigorous hours, when down the iron lane
The redbreast looks in vain
    For hips and haws,
Lo, shining flower upon my window pane
    The silver pencil of the winter draws.

When all the snowy hill
And the bare woods are still;
When snipes are silent in the frozen bogs,
    And all the garden garth is whelmed in mire
Lo, by the hearth, the laughter of the logs—
    More fair than roses, lo, the flowers of fire!

Saranac Lake

TO KALAKAUA

(With the gift of a pearl)

THE Silver Ship, my King—that was her name
In the bright islands whence your fathers came—
The Silver Ship, at rest from winds and tides,
Below your palace in your harbour rides.
And the seafarers, sitting safe on shore,
Like eager merchants count their treasures o'er.
One gift they find, one strange and lovely thing,
Now doubly precious since it pleased a king.

The right, my liege, is ancient as the lyre
For bards to give to kings what kings admire.
'Tis mine to offer for Apollo's sake;
And since the gift is fitting, yours to take.
To golden hands the golden pearl I bring:
The ocean jewel to the island king.

HONOLULU, 1889

IN MEMORIAM, E. H.

I KNEW a silver head was bright beyond compare,
I knew a queen of toil with a crown of silver hair.
Garland of valour and sorrow, of beauty and renown,
Life, that honours the brave, crowned her himself with the crown.

The beauties of youth are frail, but this was a jewel of age.
Life, that delights in the brave, gave it himself for a gauge.
Fair was the crown to behold, and beauty its poorest part—
At once the scar of the wound and the order pinned on the heart.

The beauties of man are frail, and the silver lies in the dust,
And the queen that we call to mind sleeps with the brave and the just;
Sleeps with the weary at length; but honoured and ever fair,
Shines in the eyes of the mind the crown of the silver hair.

HONOLULU

TO THE MUSE

RESIGN the rhapsody, the dream,
To men of larger reach;
Be ours the quest of a plain theme,
The piety of speech.

As monkish scribes from morning break
Toiled till the close of light,
Nor thought a day too long to make
One line or letter bright:

We also with an ardent mind,
Time, wealth, and fame forgot,
Our glory in our patience find
And skim, and skim the pot:

Till last, when round the house we hear
The evening song of birds,
One corner of blue heaven appears
In our clear well of words.

Leave, leave it then, muse of my heart!
Sans finish and sans frame,
Leave unadorned by needless art
The picture as it came.

APEMAMA

TO S. C.

I HEARD the pulse of the besieging sea
Throb far away all night. I heard the wind
Fly crying and convulse tumultuous palms.
I rose and strolled. The isle was all bright sand,
And flailing fans and shadows of the palm;
The heaven all moon and wind and the blind vault;
The keenest planet slain, for Venus slept.
    The king, my neighbour, with his host of wives,
Slept in the precinct of the palisade;
Where single, in the wind, under the moon,
Among the slumbering cabins, blazed a fire,
Sole street-lamp and the only sentinel.
    To other lands and nights my fancy turned—
To London first, and chiefly to your house,
The many-pillared and the well-beloved.
There yearning fancy lighted; there again
In the upper room I lay, and heard far off
The unsleeping city murmur like a shell;
The muffled tramp of the Museum guard
Once more went by me; I beheld again
Lamps vainly brighten the dispeopled street;

Again I longed for the returning morn,
The awaking traffic, the bestirring birds,
The consentaneous trill of tiny song
That weaves round monumental cornices
A passing charm of beauty. Most of all,
For your light foot I wearied, and your knock
That was the glad reveille of my day.

Lo, now, when to your task in the great house
At morning through the portico you pass,
One moment glance, where by the pillared wall
Far-voyaging island gods, begrimed with smoke,
Sit now unworshipped, the rude monument
Of faiths forgot and races undivined;
Sit now disconsolate, remembering well
The priest, the victim, and the songful crowd.
The blaze of the blue noon, and that huge voice
Incessant, of the breakers on the shore.
As far as these from their ancestral shrine,
So far, so foreign, your divided friends
Wander, estranged in body, not in mind.

Apemama

TROPIC RAIN

As the single pang of the blow, when the metal is mingled well,
Rings and lives and resounds in all the bounds of the bell:
So the thunder above spoke with a single tongue,
So in the heart of the mountain the sound of it rumbled and clung.

Sudden the thunder was drowned—quenched was the levin light . . .
And the angel-spirit of rain laughed out loud in the night.
Loud as the maddened river raves in the cloven glen,
Angel of rain! you laughed and leaped on the roofs of men;
And the sleepers sprang in their beds, and joyed and feared as you fell.

You struck, and my cabin quailed; the roof of it roared
like a bell,
You spoke, and at once the mountain shouted and shook
with brooks.
You ceased, and the day returned, rosy, with virgin looks.
And methought that beauty and terror are only one,
not two;
And the world has room for love, and death, and thunder,
and dew;
And all the sinews of hell slumber in summer air;
And the face of God is a rock, but the face of the rock
is fair.
Beneficent streams of tears flow at the finger of pain;
And out of the cloud that smites, beneficent rivers of rain.

VAILIMA

TO MOTHER MARYANNE

To see the infinite pity of this place,
The mangled limb, the devastated face,
The innocent sufferer smiling at the rod—
A fool were tempted to deny his God.
He sees, he shrinks. But if he gaze again,
Lo, beauty springing from the breast of pain!
He marks the sisters on the mournful shores;
And even a fool is silent and adores.

GUEST HOUSE, KALAWAO, MOLOKAI

AN END OF TRAVEL

LET now your soul in this substantial world
Some anchor strike. Be here the body moored.
This spectacle immutably from now
The picture in your eye; and when time strikes,
And the green scene goes on the instant blind,
The ultimate helpers, where your horse today
Conveyed you dreaming, bear your body dead.

VAILIMA

WE UNCOMMISERATE PASS INTO THE NIGHT

We uncommiserate pass into the night
From the loud banquet, and departing leave
A tremor in men's memories, faint and sweet
And frail as music. Features of our face,
The tones of the voice, the touch of the loved hand,
Perish and vanish, one by one, from earth.
Meanwhile, in the hall of song, the multitude
Applauds the new performer. One, perchance,
One ultimate survivor lingers on,
And smiles, and to his ancient heart recalls
The long forgotten. Ere the morrow die,
He too, returning, through the curtain comes,
And the new age forgets us and goes on.

TO PRINCESS KAIULANI

FORTH from her land to mine she goes,
The island maid, the island rose,
Light of heart and bright of face;
The daughter of a double race.
Her islands here, in Southern sun,
Shall mourn their Kaiulani gone,
And I, in her dear banyan shade,
Look vainly for my little maid.
But our Scots islands far away
Shall glitter with unwonted day,
And cast for once their tempests by
To smile in Kaiulani's eye.

HONOLULU

Written in April to Kaiulani in the April of her age; and at Waikiki, within easy walk of Kaiulani's banyan! When she comes to my land and her father's, and the rain beats upon the window (as I fear it will), let her look at this page; it will be like a weed gathered and pressed at home; and she will remember her own islands, and the shadow of the mighty tree; and she will hear the peacocks screaming in the dusk and the wind blowing in the palms; and she will think of her father sitting there alone.
—R. L. S.

EVENSONG

THE embers of the day are red
Beyond the murky hill.
The kitchen smokes: the bed
In the darkling house is spread.
The great sky darkens overhead,
And the great woods are shrill.
So far have I been led,
Lord, by Thy will:
So far I have followed, Lord, and wondered still.

The breeze from the embalmèd land
Blows sudden toward the shore,
And claps my cottage door.
I hear the signal, Lord—I understand.
The night at Thy command
Comes. I will eat and sleep and will not question more.

VAILIMA

SING ME A SONG

SING me a song of a lad that is gone,
Say, could that lad be I?
Merry of soul he sailed on a day
Over the sea to Skye.

Mull was astern, Rum on the port,
Egg on the starboard bow;
Glory of youth glowed in his soul:
Where is that glory now?

Sing me a song of a lad that is gone,
Say, could that lad be I?
Merry of soul he sailed on a day
Over the sea to Skye.

Give me again all that was there,
Give me the sun that shone!
Give me the eyes, give me the soul,
Give me the lad that's gone!

Sing me a song of a lad that is gone,
Say, could that lad be I?
Merry of soul he sailed on a day
Over the sea to Skye.

Billow and breeze, islands and seas,
Mountains of rain and sun,
All that was good, all that was fair,
All that was me is gone.

A VISIT FROM THE SEA

FAR from the loud sea beaches
Where he goes fishing and crying,
Here in the inland garden
Why is the sea-gull flying?

Here are no fish to dive for;
Here is the corn and lea;
Here are the green trees rustling.
Hie away home to sea!

Fresh is the river water
And quiet among the rushes:
This is no home for the sea-gull
But for the rooks and thrushes.

Pity the bird that has wandered!
Pity the sailor ashore!
Hurry him home to the ocean,
Let him come here no more!

High on the sea-cliff ledges
    The white gulls are trooping and crying,
Here among rooks and roses,
    Why is the sea-gull flying?

TO WILL H. LOW

YOUTH now flees on feathered foot,
Faint and fainter sounds the flute,
Rarer songs of gods; and still
Somewhere on the sunny hill,
Or along the winding stream,
Through the willows, flits a dream.
Flits, but shows a smiling face,
Flees, but with so quaint a grace,
None can choose to stay at home,
All must follow, all must roam.

This is unborn beauty. She
Now in air floats high and free,
Takes the sun and breaks the blue.
Late with stooping pinion flew
Raking hedgerow trees, and wet

Her wing in silver streams, and set
Shining foot on temple roof:
Now again she flies aloof,
Coasting mountain clouds and kiss't
By the evening's amethyst.

In wet wood and miry lane,
Still we pant and pound in vain;
Still with leaden foot we chase
Waning pinion, fainting face;
Still with grey hair we stumble on,
Till, behold, the vision gone!
Where hath fleeting beauty led?
To the doorway of the dead.
Life is over, life was gay:
We have come the primrose way.

TO H. F. BROWN

(Written during a dangerous sickness)

I sɪᴛ and wait a pair of oars
On cis-Elysian river-shores.
Where the immortal dead have sate,
'Tis mine to sit and meditate;
To re-ascend life's rivulet,
Without remorse, without regret;
And sing my *Alma Genetrix*
Among the willows of the Styx.

And lo, as my serener soul
Did these unhappy shores patrol,
And wait with an attentive ear
The coming of the gondolier,
Your fire-surviving roll I took,
Your spirited and happy book;*
Whereon, despite my frowning fate,
It did my soul so recreate
That all my fancies fled away
On a Venetian holiday.

Now, thanks to your triumphant care,
Your pages clear as April air,
The sails, the bells, the birds, I know,
And the far-off Friulan snow;
The land and sea, the sun and shade,
And the blue evening lamp-inlaid.
For this, for these, for all, O friend,
For your whole book from end to end—
For Paron Piero's muttonham—
I your defaulting debtor am.

Perchance, reviving, yet may I
To your sea-paven city hie,
And in a *felze*, some day yet
Light at your pipe my cigarette.

**Life on the Lagoons,* by H. F. Brown, originally burned in the fire at Messrs. Kegan Paul, Trench & Co.'s.

TO ANDREW LANG

Dear Andrew, with the brindled hair,
Who glory to have thrown in air,
High over arm, the trembling reed,
By Ale and Kail, by Till and Tweed:
An equal craft of hand you show
The pen to guide, the fly to throw.
I count you happy starred; for God,
When He with inkpot and with rod
Endowed you, bade your fortune lead
Forever by the crooks of Tweed,
Forever by the woods of song
And lands that to the Muse belong;
Or if in peopled streets, or in
The abhorred pedantic sanhedrim,
It should be yours to wander, still
Airs of the morn, airs of the hill,

The plovery Forest and the seas
That break about the Hebrides,
Should follow over field and plain
And find you at the window pane;
And you again see hill and peel,
And the bright spring gush at your heel.
So went the fiat forth, and so
Garrulous like a brook you go,
With sound of happy mirth and sheen
Of daylight—whether by the green
You fare that moment, or the grey;
Whether you dwell in March or May;
Or whether treat of reels and rods
Or of the old unhappy gods.
Still like a brook your page has shone,
And your ink sings of Helicon.

THE MIRROR SPEAKS

WHERE the bells peal far at sea
Cunning fingers fashioned me.
There on palace walls I hung
While that Consuelo sung.
But I heard, though I listened well,
Never a note, never a trill,
Never a beat of the chiming bell.
There I hung and looked, and there
In my grey face, faces fair
Shone from under shining hair.
Well I saw the poising head,
But the lips moved and nothing said;
And when lights were in the hall,
Silent moved the dancers all.

So awhile I glowed, and then
Fell on dusty days and men;
Long I slumbered packed in straw,
Long I none but dealers saw;
Till before my silent eye
One that sees came passing by.
Now with an outlandish grace,
To the sparkling fire I face
In the blue room at Skerryvore;
Where I wait until the door
Open, and the Prince of Men,
Henry James, shall come again.

KATHARINE

We see you as we see a face
That trembles in a forest place
Upon the mirror of a pool
Forever quiet, clear and cool;
And in the wayward glass, appears
To hover between smiles and tears,
Elfin and human, airy and true,
And backed by the reflected blue.

TO F. J. S.

I READ, dear friend, in your dear face
Your life's tale, told with perfect grace.
The river of your life, I trace
Up the sun-chequered, devious bed
To the far-distant fountain-head.

Not one quick beat of your warm heart,
Nor thought that came to you apart,
Pleasure nor pity, love nor pain
Nor sorrow, has gone by in vain.

But as some lone, wood-wandering child
Brings home with him at evening mild
The thorns and flowers of all the wild,
From your whole life, O fair and true
Your flowers and thorns you bring with you!

IT IS NOT YOURS, O MOTHER

It is not yours, O mother, to complain,
Not, mother, yours to weep,
Though nevermore your son again
Shall to your bosom creep,
Though nevermore again you watch your baby sleep.

Though in the greener paths of earth,
Mother and child, no more
We wander; and no more the birth
Of me whom once you bore,
Seems still the brave reward that once it seemed of yore.

Though as all passes, day and night,
The seasons and the years,
From you, O mother, this delight,
This also disappears—
Some profit yet survives of all your pangs and tears.

The child, the seed, the grain of corn,
The acorn on the hill,
Each for some separate end is born
In season fit, and still
Each must in strength arise to work the Almighty will.

So from the hearth the children flee,
By that Almighty hand
Austerely led; so one by sea
Goes forth, and one by land;
Nor aught of all man's sons escapes from that command.

So from the sally each obeys
The unseen Almighty nod;
So till the ending all their ways
Blindfolded loth have trod:
Nor knew their task at all, but were the tools of God.

And as the fervent smith of yore
Beat out the glowing blade,
Nor wielded in the front of war
The weapons that he made,
But in the tower at home still plied his ringing trade;

So like a sword the son shall roam
On nobler missions sent;
And as the smith remained at home
In peaceful turret pent,
So sits the while at home the mother well content.

THE SICK CHILD

Child. O MOTHER, lay your hand on my brow!
O mother, mother, where am I now?
Why is the room so gaunt and great?
Why am I lying awake so late?

Mother. Fear not at all: the night is still.
Nothing is here that means you ill—
Nothing but lamps the whole town through,
And never a child awake but you.

Child. Mother, mother, speak low in my ear,
Some of the things are so great and near,
Some are so small and far away,
I have a fear that I cannot say.
What have I done, and what do I fear,
And why are you crying, mother dear?

Mother. Out in the city, sounds begin;
Thank the kind God, the carts come in!
An hour or two more and God is so kind,
The day shall be blue in the window-blind,
Then shall my child go sweetly asleep,
And dream of the birds and the hills of sheep.

SING CLEARLIER, MUSE

SING clearlier, Muse, or evermore be still,
Sing truer or no longer sing!
No more the voice of melancholy Jacques
To wake a weeping echo in the hill;
But as the boy, the pirate of the spring,
From the green elm a living linnet takes,
One natural verse recapture—then be still.

A CAMP

From *Travels with a Donkey.*

THE bed was made, the room was fit,
By punctual eve the stars were lit;
The air was still, the water ran,
No need was there for maid or man.
When we put up, my ass and I,
At God's green caravanserai.

TO MY FATHER

PEACE and her huge invasion to these shores
Puts daily home; innumerable sails
Dawn on the far horizon and draw near;
Innumerable loves, uncounted hopes
To our wild coasts, not darkling now, approach.
Not now obscure, since thou and thine are there,
And bright on the lone isle, the foundered reef,
The long, resounding foreland, Pharos stands.

These are thy works, O father, these thy crown:
Whether on high the air be pure, they shine
Along the yellowing sunset, and all night
Among the unnumbered stars of God they shine:
Or whether fogs arise and far and wide
The low sea-level drown—each finds a tongue
And all night long the tolling bell resounds:
So shine, so toll, till night be overpast,
Till the stars vanish, till the sun return,
And in the haven rides the fleet secure.

In the first hour, the seaman in his skiff
Moves through the unmoving bay, to where the town
Its earliest smoke into the air upbreathes
And the rough hazels climb along the beach.
To the tugged oar the distant echo speaks.
The ship lies resting, where by reef and roost
Thou and thy lights have led her like a child.

This hast thou done, and I—can I be base?
I must arise, O father, and to port
Some lost, complaining seaman pilot home.

A PORTRAIT

I AM a kind of farthing dip,
Unfriendly to the nose and eyes;
A blue-behinded ape, I skip
Upon the trees of Paradise.

At mankind's feast, I take my place
In solemn, sanctimonious state,
And have the air of saying grace
While I defile the dinner plate.

I am "the smiler with the knife,"
The battener upon garbage, I—
Dear Heaven, with such a rancid life,
Were it not better far to die?

Yet still, about the human pale,
I love to scamper, love to race,
To swing by my irreverent tail
All over the most holy place;

And when at length, some golden day,
The unfailing sportsman, aiming at,
Shall bag, me—all the world shall say:
Thank God, and there's an end of that!

MY HOUSE, I SAY

My house, I say. But hark to the sunny doves
That make my roof the arena of their loves,
That gyre about the gable all day long
And fill the chimneys with their murmurous song:
Our house, they say; and *mine,* the cat declares
And spreads his golden fleece upon the chairs;
And *mine* the dog, and rises stiff with wrath
If any alien foot profane the path.
So, too, the buck that trimmed my terraces,
Our whilom gardener, called the garden his;
Who now, deposed, surveys my plain abode
And his late kingdom, only from the road.

SAY NOT OF ME

SAY not of me that weakly I declined
The labours of my sires, and fled the sea,
The towers we founded and the lamps we lit
To play at home with paper like a child.
But rather say: *In the afternoon of time*
A strenuous family dusted from its hands
The sand of granite, and beholding far
Along the sounding coast its pyramids
And tall memorials catch the dying sun,
Smiled well content, and to this childish task
Around the fire addressed its evening hours.

OUR LADY OF THE SNOWS

Out of the sun, out of the blast,
Out of the world, alone I passed
Across the moor and through the wood
To where the monastery stood.
There neither lute nor breathing fife,
Nor rumour of the world of life,
Nor confidences low and dear,
Shall strike the meditative ear.
Aloof, unhelpful, and unkind,
The prisoners of the iron mind,
Where nothing speaks except the bell
The unfraternal brothers dwell.
Poor passionate men, still clothed afresh
With agonising folds of flesh;
Whom the clear eyes solicit still
To some bold output of the will,
While fairy Fancy far before
And musing Memory-Hold-the-door
Now to heroic death invite
And now uncurtain fresh delight.
O, little boots it thus to dwell
On the remote unneighboured hill!
O to be up and doing, O
Unfearing and unshamed to go
In all the uproar and the press
About my human business!

My undissuaded heart I hear
Whisper courage in my ear.

With voiceless calls, the ancient earth
Summons me to a daily birth;
Thou, O my love, ye, O my friends–
The gist of life, the end of ends–
To laugh, to love, to live, to die,
Ye call me by the ear and eye!

Forth from the casemate, on the plain
Where honour has the world to gain,
Pour forth and bravely do your part,
O knights of the unshielded heart!
Forth and forever forward! Out
From prudent turret and redoubt,
And in the melee charge amain.
To fall but yet to rise again!
Captive? ah, still, to honour bright,
A captive soldier of the right!
Or free and fighting, good with ill?
Unconquering but unconquered still!

And ye, O brethren, what if God,
When from Heav'n's top he spies abroad,
And sees on this tormented stage
The noble war of mankind rage;
What if his vivifying eye,

O monks, should pass your corner by?
For still the Lord is Lord of might;
In deeds, in deeds, he takes delight;
The plough, the spear, the laden barks,
The field, the founded city, marks;
He marks the smiler of the streets,
The singer upon garden seats;
He sees the climber in the rocks;
To him, the shepherd folds his flocks.

For those he loves that underprop
With daily virtues Heaven's top,
And bear the falling sky with ease,
Unfrowning caryatides.
Those he approves that ply the trade,
That rock the child, that wed the maid,
That with weak virtues, weaker hands,
Sow gladness on the peopled lands,
And still with laughter, song and shout,
Spin the great wheel of earth about.

But ye?—O ye who linger still
Here in your fortress on the hill,
With placid face, with tranquil breath,
The unsought volunteers of death,
Our cheerful General on high
With careless looks may pass you by.

TO W. E. HENLEY

THE year runs through her phases; rain and sun,
Springtime and summer pass; winter succeeds;
But one pale season rules the house of death.
Cold falls the imprisoned daylight; fell disease
By each lean pallet squats, and pain and sleep
Toss gaping on the pillows.

But O thou!
Uprise and take thy pipe. Bid music flow,
Strains by good thoughts attended, like the spring
The swallows follow over land and sea.
Pain sleeps at once; at once, with open eyes,
Dozing despair awakes. The shepherd sees
His flock come bleating home; the seaman hears
Once more the cordage rattle. Airs of home!
Youth, love and roses blossom; the gaunt ward
Dislimns and disappears, and, opening out,
Shows brooks and forests, and the blue beyond
Of mountains.

Small the pipe; but O! do thou,
Peak-faced and suffering piper, blow therein
The dirge of heroes dead; and to these sick,
These dying, sound the triumph over death.
Behold! each greatly breathes; each tastes a joy
Unknown before, in dying; for each knows
A hero dies with him—though unfulfilled,
Yet conquering truly—and not dies in vain.

So is pain cheered, death comforted. The house
Of sorrow smiles to listen. Once again—
O thou, Orpheus and Heracles, the bard
And the deliverer touch the stops again!

TO A GARDENER

FRIEND, in my mountain-side domain,
My plain-beholding, rosy, green
And linnet-haunted garden-ground,
Let still the esculents abound.
Let first the onion flourish there,
Rose among roots, the maiden-fair,
Wine-scented and poetic soul
Of the capacious salad bowl.
Let thyme the mountaineer (to dress
The tinier birds) and wading cress,
The lover of the shallow brook,
From all my plots and borders look.
Nor crisp and ruddy radish, nor
Pease-pods for the child's pinafore
Be lacking; nor of salad clan
The last and least that ever ran
About great nature's garden-beds.
Nor thence be missed the speary heads
Of artichoke; nor thence the bean
That gathered innocent and green
Outsavours the belauded pea.

These tend, I prithee; and for me,
Thy most long-suffering master, bring
In April, when the linnets sing
And the days lengthen more and more,
At sundown to the garden door.
And I, being provided thus,
Shall, with superb asparagus,
A book, a taper, and a cup
Of country wine, divinely sup.

LA SOLITUDE, HYERE

TO MINNIE

(With a hand-glass)

A PICTURE-FRAME for you to fill,
    A paltry setting for your face,
A thing that has no worth until
    You lend it something of your grace,

I send (unhappy I that sing
    Laid by awhile upon the shelf)
Because I would not send a thing
    Less charming than you are yourself.

And happier than I, alas!
    (Dumb thing, I envy its delight)
'Twill wish you well, the looking-glass,
    And look you in the face tonight.

HENRY JAMES

WHO comes tonight? We ope the doors in vain.
Who comes? My bursting walls, can you contain
The presences that now together throng
Your narrow entry, as with flowers and song,
As with the air of life, the breath of talk?
Lo, how these fair immaculate women walk
Behind their jocund maker; and we see
Slighted *De Mauves,* and that far different she,
Gressie, the trivial sphynx: and to our feast
Daisy and *Barb* and *Chancellor* (she not least!)
With all their silken, all their airy kin,
Do like unbidden angels enter in
But he, attended by these shining names,
Comes (best of all) himself—our welcome James.

IF THIS WERE FAITH

God, if this were enough,
That I see things bare to the buff
And up to the buttocks in mire;
That I ask nor hope nor hire,
Nut in the husk,
Nor dawn beyond the dusk,
Nor life beyond death:
God, if this were faith?

Having felt thy wind in my face
Spit sorrow and disgrace,
Having seen thine evil doom
In Golgotha and Khartoum,
And the brutes, the work of thine hands,
Fill with injustice lands
And stain with blood the sea:
If still in my veins the glee
Of the black night and the sun
And the lost battle, run:
If, an adept,
The iniquitous lists I still accept
With joy, and joy to endure and be withstood,
And still to battle and perish for a dream of good:
God, if that were enough?

If to feel, in the ink of the slough,
And the sink of the mire,
Veins of glory and fire
Run through and transpierce and transpire,
And a secret purpose of glory in every part,
And the answering glory of battle fill my heart;
To thrill with the joy of girded men
To go on forever and fail and go on again,
And be mauled to the earth and arise,
And contend for the shade of a word and a thing not
not seen with the eyes:
With the half of a broken hope for a pillow at night
That somehow the right is the right
And the smooth shall bloom from the rough:
Lord, if that were enough?

MY WIFE

Trusty, dusky, vivid, true,
With eyes of gold and bramble-dew,
    Steel-true and blade-straight,
The great Artificer
    Made my mate.

Honour, anger, valour, fire;
A love that life could never tire,
    Death quench or evil stir,
The mighty Master
    Gave to her.

Teacher, tender comrade, wife,
A fellow-farer true through life,
    Heart-whole and soul-free
The august Father
    Gave to me.

I KNOW NOT HOW IT IS WITH YOU

I KNOW not how it is with you—
  I love the first and last,
The whole field of the present view,
  The whole flow of the past.

One tittle of the things that are,
  Nor you should change nor I—
One pebble in our path—one star
  In all our heaven of sky.

Our lives, and every day and hour,
  One symphony appear:
One road, one garden—every flower
  And every bramble dear.

A SONG OF THE ROAD

THE gauger walked with willing foot,
And aye the gauger played the flute;
And what should Master Gauger play
But *Over the hills and far away?*

Whene'er I buckle on my pack
And foot it gaily in the track,
O pleasant gauger, long since dead,
I hear you fluting on ahead.

You go with me the self-same way—
The self-same air for me you play;
For I do think and so do you
It is the tune to travel to.

For who would gravely set his face
To go to this or t'other place?
There's nothing under heaven so blue
That's fairly worth the travelling to.

On every hand the roads begin,
And people walk with zeal therein;
But wheresoe'er the highways tend,
Be sure there's nothing at the end.

Then follow you, wherever hie
The travelling mountains of the sky.
Or let the streams in civil mode
Direct your choice upon a road;

For one and all, or high or low,
Will lead you where you wish to go;
And one and all go night and day
Over the hills and far away!

FOREST OF MONTARGIS, 1878

INTRODUCTION

This tale, of which I have not consciously changed a single feature, I received from tradition. It is highly popular through all the country of the eight Tevas, the clan to which Rahéro belonged; and particularly in Taiárapu, the windward peninsula of Tahiti, where he lived. I have heard from end to end two versions; and as many as five different persons have helped me with details. There seems no reason why the tale should not be true.

THE SONG OF RAHÉRO

A LEGEND OF TAHITI

I. THE SLAYING OF TÁMATÉA

IT fell in the days of old, as the men of Taiárapu tell,
A youth went forth to the fishing, and fortune favoured him well.
Támatéa his name: gullible, simple, and kind,
Comely of countenance, nimble of body, empty of mind,
His mother ruled him and loved him beyond the wont of a wife,
Serving the lad for eyes and living herself in his life.

Alone from the sea and the fishing came Támatéa the fair,
Urging his boat to the beach, and the mother awaited him there,
—"Long may you live!" said she. "Your fishing has sped to a wish.

And now let us choose for the king the fairest of all your fish.
For fear inhabits the palace and grudging grows in the land,
Marked is the sluggardly foot and marked the niggardly hand,
The hours and the miles are counted, the tributes numbered and weighed,
And woe to him that comes short, and woe to him that delayed!"
So spoke on the beach the mother, and counselled the wiser thing.
For Rahéro stirred in the country and secretly mined the king.
Nor were the signals wanting of how the leaven wrought,
In the cords of obedience loosed and the tributes grudgingly brought.
And when last to the temple of Oro the boat with the victim sped,
And the priest uncovered the basket and looked on the face of the dead,
Trembling fell upon all at sight of an ominous thing,
For there was the aito[1] dead, and he of the house of the king.

So spake on the beach the mother, matter worthy of note,
And wattled a basket well, and chose a fish from the boat;
And Támatéa the pliable shouldered the basket and went,

And travelled, and sang as he travelled, a lad that was well content.
Still the way of his going was round by the roaring coast,
Where the ring of the reef is broke and the trades run riot the most.
On his left, with smoke as of battle, the billows battered the land;
Unscalable, turretted mountains rose on the inner hand.
And cape, and village, and river, and vale, and mountain above,
Each had a name in the land of men to remember and love;
And never the name of a place, but lo! a song in its praise:
Ancient and unforgotten, songs of the earlier days,
That the elders taught to the young, and at night, in the full of the moon,
Garlanded boys and maidens sang together in tune.
Támatéa the placable went with a lingering foot;
He sung as loud as a bird, he whistled hoarse as a flute;
He broiled in the sun, he breathed in the grateful shadow of trees,
In the icy stream of the rivers he waded over the knees;
And still in his empty mind crowded, a thousand-fold,
The deeds of the strong and the songs of the cunning heroes of old.

And now was he come to a place Taiárapu honoured the most,

Where a silent valley of woods debouched on the noisy
coast,
Spewing a level river. There was a haunt of Pai.[2]
There, in his potent youth, when his parents drove him to
die,
Honoura lived like a beast, lacking the lamp and the fire,
Washed by the rains of the trade and clotting his hair
in the mire;
And there, so mighty his hands, he bent the tree to his
foot—
So keen the spur of his hunger, he plucked it naked of
fruit.

There, as she pondered the clouds for the shadow of
coming ills,
Ahupu, the woman of song, walked on high on the hills.

Of these was Rahéro sprung, a man of a godly race;
And inherited cunning of spirit and beauty of body and
face.
Of yore in his youth, as an aito, Rahéro wandered the
land,
Delighting maids with his tongue, smiting men with his
hand.
Famous he was in his youth; but before the midst of his
life
Paused, and fashioned a song of farewell to glory and
strife.

House of mine (it went), *house upon the sea,*
Beloved of all my fathers, more beloved by me!
Vale of the strong Honoura, deep ravine of Pai,
Again in your woody summits I hear the trade-wind cry.

House of mine, in your walls, strong sounds the sea,
Of all sounds on earth, dearest sound to me.
I have heard the applause of men, I have heard it arise and die;
Sweeter now in my house I hear the trade-wind cry.

These were the words of his singing, other the thought of his heart;
For secret desire of glory vexed him, dwelling apart.
Lazy and crafty he was, and loved to lie in the sun,
And loved the cackle of talk and the true word uttered in fun;

Lazy he was, his roof was ragged, his table was lean,
And the fish swam safe in his sea, and he gathered the near and the green.
He sat in his house and laughed, but he loathed the king of the land,
And he uttered the grudging word under the covering hand.
Treason spread from his door; and he looked for a day to come,

A day of the crowding people, a day of the summoning drum,
When the vote should be taken, the king be driven forth in disgrace,
And Rahéro, the laughing and lazy, sit and rule in his place.
Here Támatéa came, and beheld the house on the brook;
And Rahéro was there by the way and covered an oven to cook.[3]
Naked he was to the loins, but the tattoo covered the lack,
And the sun and the shadow of palms dappled his muscular back.
Swiftly he lifted his head at the fall of the coming feet,
And the water sprang in his mouth with a sudden desire of meat;
For he marked the basket carried, covered from flies and the sun;[4]
And Rahéro buried his fire, but the meat in his house was none.

Forth he stepped; and took, and delayed the boy, by the hand;
And vaunted the joys of meat and the ancient ways of the land:

—"Our sires of old in Taiárapu, they that created the race,
Ate ever with eager hand; nor regarded season or place,

Ate in the boat at the oar, on the way afoot; and at night
Arose in the midst of dreams to rummage the house for a bite.
It is good for the youth in his turn to follow the way of the sire;
And behold how fitting the time! for here do I cover my fire."
—"I see the fire for the cooking but never the meat to cook,"
Said Támatéa.—"Tut!" said Rahéro. "Here in the brook
And there in the tumbling sea, the fishes are thick as flies,
Hungry like healthy men, and like pigs for savour and size:
Crayfish crowding the river, sea-fish thronging the sea."
—"Well it may be," says the other, "and yet be nothing to me.
Fain would I eat, but alas! I have needful matter in hand,
Since I carry my tribute of fish to the jealous king of the land."
Now at the word a light sprang in Rahéro's eyes.
"I will gain me a dinner," thought he, "and lend the king a surprise."
And he took the lad by the arm, as they stood by the side of the track,
And smiled, and rallied, and flattered, and pushed him forward and back.
It was "You that sing like a bird, I never have heard you sing,"

And "The lads when I was a lad were none so feared
of a king.
And of what account is an hour, when the heart is empty
of guile?
But come, and sit in the house and laugh with the women
awhile;
And I will but drop my hook, and behold! the dinner
made."

So Támatéa the pliable hung up his fish in the shade
On a tree by the side of the way; and Rahéro carried
him in,
Smiling as smiles the fowler when flutters the bird to the
gin,
And chose him a shining hook,[5] and viewed it with
sedulous eye,
And breathed and burnished it well on the brawn of his
naked thigh,
And set a mat for the gull, and bade him be merry and
bide,
Like a man concerned for his guest, and the fishing, and
nothing beside.
Now when Rahéro was forth, he paused and hearkened,
and heard
The gull jest in the house and the women laugh at his
word;
And stealthily crossed to the side of the way, to the shady
place

Where the basket hung on a mango; and craft transfigured his face.
Deftly he opened the basket, and took of the fat of the fish,
The cut of kings and chieftains, enough for a goodly dish.

This he wrapped in a leaf, set on the fire to cook
And buried; and next the marred remains of the tribute he took,
And doubled and packed them well, and covered the basket close
"There is a buffet, my king," quoth he, "and a nauseous dose!"
And hung the basket again in the shade, in a cloud of flies
"And there is a sauce to your dinner, king of the crafty eyes!"

Soon as the oven was open, the fish smelt excellent good.
In the shade, by the house of Rahéro, down they sat to their food,
And cleared the leaves[6] in silence, or uttered a jest and laughed,
And raising the cocoanut bowls, buried their faces and quaffed.
But chiefly in silence they ate; and soon as the meal was done,

Rahéro feigned to remember and measured the hour by the sun,
And "Támatéa," quoth he, "it is time to be jogging, my lad."

So Támatéa arose, doing ever the thing he was bade,
And carelessly shouldered the basket, and kindly saluted his host;
And again the way of his going was round by the roaring coast.
Long he went; and at length was aware of a pleasant green,
And the stems and shadows of palms, and roofs of lodges between.
There sate, in the door of his palace, the king on a kingly seat,
And aitos stood armed around, and the yottowas[7] sat at his feet.
But fear was a worm in his heart: fear darted his eyes;
And he probed men's faces for treasons and pondered their speech for lies.
To him came Támatéa, the basket slung in his hand,
And paid him the due obeisance standing as vassals stand.
In silence hearkened the king, and closed the eyes in his face,
Harbouring odious thoughts and the baseless fears of the base;

In silence accepted the gift and sent the giver away.
So Támatéa departed, turning his back on the day.
And lo, as the king sat brooding, a rumour rose in the crowd;
The yottowas nudged and whispered, the commons murmured aloud;
Tittering fell upon all at sight of the impudent thing,
At the sight of a gift unroyal flung in the face of a king.
And the face of the king turned white and red with anger and shame
In their midst; and the heart in his body was water and then was flame;
Till of a sudden, turning, he gripped an aito hard,
A youth that stood with his ómare,[8] one of the daily guard,
And spat in his ear a command, and pointed and uttered a name,
And hid in the shade of the house his impotent anger and shame.

Now Támatéa the fool was far on the homeward way,
The rising night in his face, behind him the dying day.
Rahéro saw him go by, and the heart of Rahéro was glad,
Devising shame to the king and nowise harm to the lad;
And all that dwelt by the way saw and saluted him well,
For he had the face of a friend and the news of the town to tell;

And pleased with the notice of folk, and pleased that his journey was done,
Támatéa drew homeward, turning his back to the sun.
And now was the hour of the bath in Taiárapu; far and near
The lovely laughter of bathers rose and delighted his ear.
Night massed in the valleys; the sun on the mountain coast
Struck, end-long; and above the clouds embattled their host,
And glowed and gloomed on the heights; and the heads of the palms were gems,
And far to the rising eve extended the shade of their stems;
And the shadow of Támatéa hovered already at home.
And sudden the sound of one coming and running light as the foam
Struck on his ear; and he turned, and lo! a man on his track,
Girded and armed with an ómare, following hard at his back.
At a bound the man was upon him; and, or ever a word was said,
The loaded end of the ómare fell and laid him dead.

II. THE VENGING OF TÁMATÉA

Thus was Rahéro's treason; thus and no further it sped:
The king sat safe in his place and a kindly fool was dead.

But the mother of Támatéa arose with death in her eyes.
All night along, and the next, Taiárapu rang with her cries.
As when a babe in the wood turns with a chill of doubt
And perceives nor home, nor friends, for the trees have closed her about,
The mountain rings and her breast is torn with the voice of despair:
So the lion-like woman idly wearied the air
For awhile, and pierced men's hearing in vain, and wounded their hearts.
But as when the weather changes at sea, in dangerous parts,
And sudden the hurricane wrack unrolls up the front of the sky,
At once the ship lies idle, the sails hang silent on high,
The breath of the wind that blew is blown out like the flame of a lamp,
And the silent armies of death draw near with inaudible tramp:
So sudden, the voice of her weeping ceased; in silence she rose

And passed from the house of her sorrow, a woman
clothed with repose,
Carrying death in her breast and sharpening death with
her hand.

Hither she went and thither in all the coasts of the land.
They tell that she feared not to slumber alone, in the
dead of night,
In accursed places; beheld, unblenched, the ribbon of
light[9]
Spin from temple to temple; guided the perilous skiff,
Abhorred not the paths of the mountain and trod the
verge of the cliff;
From end to end of the island, thought not the distance
long,
But forth from king to king carried the tale of her wrong.
To king after king, as they sat in the palace door, she
came,
Claiming kinship, declaiming verses, naming her name
And the names of all of her fathers; and still, with a heart
on the rack,
Jested to capture a hearing and laughed when they jested
back:
So would deceive them awhile, and change and return in
a breath,
And on all the men of Vaiau imprecate instant death;
And tempt her kings—for Vaiau was a rich and prosperous
land.

And flatter—for who would attempt it but warriors mighty of hand?
And change in a breath again and rise in a strain of song,
Invoking the beaten drums, beholding the fall of the strong,
Calling the fowls of the air to come and feast on the dead.
And they held the chin in silence, and heard her, and shook the head;
For they knew the men of Taiárapu famous in battle and feast,
Marvellous eaters and smiters: the men of Vaiau not least.
To the land of the Námunu-úra,[10] to Paca, at length she came,
To men who were foes to the Tevas and hated their race and name.
There was she well received, and spoke with Hiopa the king.[11]
And Hiopa listened, and weighed, and wisely considered the thing.
"Here in the back of the isle we dwell in a sheltered place,"
Quoth he to the woman, "in quiet, a weak and peaceable race.
But far in the teeth of the wind lofty Taiárapu lies;

Strong blows the wind of the trade on its seaward face, and cries
Aloud in the top of arduous mountains, and utters its song
In green continuous forests. Strong is the wind, and strong
And fruitful and hardy the race, famous in battle and feast,
Marvellous eaters and smiters: the men of Vaiau not least.
Now hearken to me, my daughter, and hear a word of the wise:
How a strength goes linked with a weakness, two by two, like the eyes.

They can wield the ómare well and cast the javelin far;
Yet are they greedy and weak as the swine and the children are.
Plant we, then, here at Paea, a garden of excellent fruits;
Plant we bananas and kava and taro, the king of roots;
Let the pigs in Paea be tapu[12] and no man fish for a year;
And of all the meat in Tahiti gather we threefold here.
So shall the fame of our plenty fill the island, and so,
At last, on the tongue of rumour, go where we wish it to go.
Then shall the pigs of Taiárapu raise their snouts in the air;
But we sit quiet and wait, as the fowler sits by the snare,

And tranquilly fold our hands, till the pigs come nosing the food:
But meanwhile build us a house of Trotéa, the stubborn wood,
Bind it with incombustible tongs, set a roof to the room,
Too strong for the hands of a man to dissever or fire to consume;
And there, when the pigs come trotting, there shall the feast be spread,
There shall the eye of the morn enlighten the feasters dead.
So be it done; for I have a heart that pities your state,
And Nateva and Námunu-úra are fire and water for hate."

All was done as he said, and the gardens prospered; and now
The fame of their plenty went out, and word of it came to Vaiau.
For the men of Námunu-úra sailed, to the windward far,
Lay in the offing by south where the towns of the Tevas are,
And cast overboard of their plenty; and lo! at the Tevas' feet
The surf on all of the beaches tumbled treasures of meat.
In the salt of the sea, a harvest tossed with the refluent foam;
And the children gleaned it in playing, and ate and carried it home;

And the elders stared and debated, and wondered and passed the jest,
But whenever a guest came by eagerly questioned the guest;
And little by little, from one to another, the word went round:
"In all the borders of Paea the victual rots on the ground,
And swine are plenty as rats. And now, when they fare to the sea,
The men of the Námunu-úra glean from under the tree
And load the canoe to the gunwale with all that is toothsome to eat;
And all day long on the sea the jaws are crushing the meat,
The steersman eats at the helm, the rowers munch at the oar,
And at length, when their bellies are full, overboard with the store!"

Now was the word made true, and soon as the bait was bare,
All the pigs of Taiárapu raised their snouts in the air.
Songs were recited, and kinship was counted, and tales were told
How war had severed of late but peace had cemented of old
The clans of the island. "To war," said they, "now set we an end,

And hie to the Námunu-úra even as a friend to a friend."

So judged, and a day was named; and soon as the morning broke,
Canoes were thrust in the sea and the houses emptied of folk.
Strong blew the wind of the south, the wind that gathers the clan;
Along all the line of the reef the clamorous surges ran;
And the clouds were piled on the top of the island mountain high,
A mountain throned on a mountain. The fleet of canoes swept by
In the midst, on the green lagoon, with a crew released from care,
Sailing an even water, breathing a summer air,
Cheered by a cloudless sun; and ever to left and right,
Bursting surge on the reef, drenching storms on the height.
So the folk of Vaiau sailed and were glad all day,
Coasting the palm-tree cape and crossing the populous bay

By all the towns of the Tevas; and still as they bowled along,
Boat would answer to boat with jest and laughter and song,

And the people of all the towns trooped to the sides of
the sea
And gazed from under the hand or sprang aloft on the
tree,
Hailing and cheering. Time failed them for more to do;
The holiday village careened to the wind, and was gone
from view
Swift as a passing bird; and ever as onward it bore,
Like the cry of the passing bird, bequeathed its song to
the shore—
Desirable laughter of maids and the cry of delight of the
child.
And the gazer, left behind, stared at the wake and smiled.
By all the towns of the Tevas they went, and Pápara last,
The home of the chief, the place of muster in war; and
passed
The march of the lands of the clan, to the lands of an
alien folk.
And there, from the dusk of the shoreside palms, a
column of smoke
Mounted and wavered and died in the gold of the setting
sun,
"Paea!" they cried. "It is Paea." And so was the voyage
done.

In the early fall of the night, Hiopa came to the shore,
And beheld and counted the comers, and lo, they were
forty score:

The pelting feet of the babes that ran already and played,
The clean-lipped smile of the boy, the slender breasts
 of the maid,
And mighty limbs of women, stalwart mothers of men.
The sires stood forth unabashed; but a little back from his
 ken
Clustered the scarcely nubile, the lads and maids, in a
 ring,
Fain of each other, afraid of themselves, aware of the
 king
And aping behaviour, but slinging together with hands
 and eyes,
With looks that were kind like kisses, and laughter tender
 as sighs.
There, too, the grandsire stood, raising his silver crest,
And the impotent hands of a suckling groped in his barren
 breast.
The childhood of love, the pair well married, the inno-
 cent brood,
The tale of the generations repeated and ever renewed—
Hiopa beheld them together, all the ages of man,
And a moment shook in his purpose.

But these were the foes of his clan,
And he trod upon pity and came, and civilly greeted the
 king,
And gravely entreated Rahéro; and for all that could
 fight or sing,

And claimed a name in the land, had fitting phrases of
praise;
But with all who were well-descended he spoke of the
ancient days.

And " 'Tis true," said he, "that in Paea the victual rots on
the ground;
But, friends, your number is many; and pigs must be
hunted and found,
And the lads troop to the mountains to bring the féis
down,
And around the bowls of the kava cluster the maids of
the town.
So, for tonight, sleep here; but king, common, and priest
Tomorrow, in order due, shall sit with me in the feast."
Sleepless the live-long night, Hiopa's followers toiled.
The pigs screamed and were slaughtered; the spars of the
guest-house oiled,
The leaves spread on the floor. In many a mountain
glen
The moon drew shadows of trees on the naked bodies of
men
Plucking and bearing fruits; and in all the bounds of the
town
Red glowed the cocoanut fires, and were buried and
trodden down.
Thus did seven of the yottowas toil with their tale of the
clan,

But the eighth wrought with his lads, hid from the sight
of man.
In the deeps of the woods they laboured, piling the fuel
high
In fagots, the load of a man, fuel seasoned and dry,
Thirsty to seize upon fire and apt to blurt into flame.

And now was the day of the feast. The forests, as morning
came,
Tossed in the wind, and the peaks quaked in the blaze
of the day
And the cocoanuts showered on the ground, rebounding
and rolling away:
A glorious morn for a feast, a famous wind for a fire.
To the hall of feasting Hiopa led them, mother and sire
And maid and babe in a tale, the whole of the holiday
throng.
Smiling they came, garlanded green, not dreaming of
wrong;
And for every three, a pig, tenderly cooked in the ground,
Waited; and féi, the staff of life, heaped in a mound
For each where he sat; for each, bananas roasted and raw
Piled with a bountiful hand, as for horses hay and straw
Are stacked in a stable; and fish, the food of desire,[13]
And plentiful vessels of sauce, and breadfruit gilt in the
fire;
And kava was common as water. Feasts have there been
ere now,

And many, but never a feast like that of the folk of Vaiau.
All day long they ate with the resolute greed of brutes,
And turned from the pigs to the fish, and again from the fish to the fruits,
And emptied the vessels of sauce, and drank of the kava deep;
Till the young lay stupid as stones, and the strongest nodded to sleep.
Sleep that was mighty as death and blind as a moonless night
Tethered them hand and foot; and their souls were drowned, and the light
Was cloaked from their eyes. Senseless together, the old and the young,
The fighter deadly to smite and the prater cunning of tongue,
The woman wedded and fruitful, inured to the pangs of birth,
And the maid that knew not of kisses, blindly sprawled on the earth.
From the hall Hiopa the king and his chiefs came stealthily forth.
Already the sun hung low and enlightened the peaks of the north;
But the wind was stubborn to die and blew as it blows at morn,
Showering the nuts in the dusk, and e'en as a banner is torn,

High on the peaks of the island, shattered the mountain cloud.
And now at once, at a signal, a silent, emulous crowd
Set hands to the work of death, hurrying to and fro,
Like ants, to furnish the fagots, building them broad and low,
And piling them high and higher around the walls of the hall.
Silence persisted within, for sleep lay heavy on all.
But the mother of Támatéa stood at Hiopa's side,
And shook for terror and joy like a girl that is a bride.
Night fell on the toilers, and first Hiopa the wise
Made the round of the house, visiting all with his eyes;
And all was piled to the eaves, and fuel blockaded the door;
And within, in the house beleaguered, slumbered the forty score.
Then was an aito dispatched and came with fire in his hand,
And Hiopa took it. "Within," said he, "is the life of a land;
And behold! I breathe on the coal, I breathe on the dales of the east,
And silence falls on forest and shore; the voice of the feast
Is quenched, and the smoke of cooking; the rooftree decays and falls

On the empty lodge, and the winds subvert deserted walls."

Therewithal, to the fuel, he laid the glowing coal;
And the redness ran in the mass and burrowed within like a mole,
And copious smoke was conceived. But, as when a dam is to burst,
The water lips it and crosses in silver trickles at first,
And then, of a sudden, whelms and bears it away forth-right:
So now, in a moment, the flame sprang and towered in the night,
And wrestled and roared in the wind, and high over house and tree,
Stood, like a streaming torch, enlightening land and sea.

But the mother of Támatéa threw her arms abroad,
"Pyre of my son," she shouted, "debited vengeance of God,
Late, late, I behold you, yet I behold you at last,
And glory, beholding! For now are the days of my agony past,
The lust that famished my soul now eats and drinks its desire,
And they that encompassed my son shrivel alive in the fire.

Tenfold precious the vengeance that comes after lingering years!
Ye quenched the voice of my singer? Hark, in your dying ears,
The song of the conflagration! Ye left me a widow alone?
Behold, the whole of your race consumes, sinew and bone
And torturing flesh together: man, mother, and maid
Heaped in a common shambles; and already, borne by the trade,
The smoke of your dissolution darkens the stars of night."
Thus she spoke, and her stature grew in the people's sight.

III. RAHÉRO

Rahéro was there in the hall asleep: beside him his wife,
Comely, a mirthful woman, one that delighted in life;
And a girl that was ripe for marriage, shy and sly as a mouse;
And a boy, a climber of trees: all the hopes of his house.
Unwary, with open hands, he slept in the midst of his folk,
And dreamed that he heard a voice crying without, and awoke,
Leaping blindly afoot like one from a dream that he fears.

A hellish glow and clouds were about him—it roared in his ears
Like the sound of the cataract fall that plunges sudden and steep;
And Rahéro swayed as he stood, and his reason was still asleep.
Now the flame struck hard on the house, wind-wielded, a fracturing blow,
And the end of the roof was burst and fell on the sleepers below;
And the lofty hall, and the feast, and the prostrate bodies of folk,
Shone red in his eyes a moment, and then were swallowed of smoke.
In the mind of Rahéro clearness came; and he opened his throat;
And as when a squall comes sudden, the straining sail of a boat
Thunders aloud and bursts, so thundered the voice of the man.
"The wind and the rain!" he shouted, the mustering word of the clan,[14]
And "up!" and "to arms, men of Vaiau!" But silence replied,
Or only the voice of the gusts of the fire, and nothing beside.

Rahéro stooped and groped. He handled his woman-kind,
But the fumes of the fire and the kava had quenched the life of their mind,

And they lay like pillars prone; and his hand encountered the boy,
And there sprang in the gloom of his soul a sudden lightning of joy.
"Him can I save!" he thought, "if I were speedy enough."
And he loosened the cloth from his loins, and swaddled the child in the stuff;
And about the strength of his neck he knotted the burden well.

There where the roof had fallen, it roared like the mouth of hell.
Thither Rahéro went, stumbling on senseless folk,
And grappled a post of the house, and began to climb in the smoke:
The last alive of Vaiau: and the son borne by the sire.
The post glowed in the grain with ulcers of eating fire.
And the fire bit to the blood and mangled his hands and thighs;
And the fumes sang in his head like wine and stung in his eyes;
And still he climbed, and came to the top, the place of proof,

And thrust a hand through the flame, and clambered alive on the roof.
But even as he did so, the wind, in a garment of flames and pain,
Wrapped him from head to heel; and the waistcloth parted in twain;
And the living fruit of his loins dropped in the fire below.
About the blazing feast-house clustered the eyes of the foe,
Watching, hand upon weapon, lest ever a soul should flee,
Shading the brow from the glare, straining the neck to see.
Only, to leeward, the flames in the wind crept far and wide,
And the forest sputtered on fire; and there might no man abide.
Thither Rahéro crept, and dropped from the burning eaves,
And crouching low to the ground, in a treble covert of leaves
And fire and volleying smoke, ran for the life of his soul
Unseen; and behind him under a furnace of ardent coal,
Cairned with a wonder of flame, and blotting the night with smoke,
Blazed and were smelted together the bones of all his folk.

He fled unguided at first; but hearing the breakers roar,
Thitherward shaped his way, and came at length to the shore.
Sound-limbed he was: dry-eyed; but smarted in every part;
And the mighty rage of his ribs heaved on his straining heart
With sorrow and rage. And "Fools!" he cried, "fools of Vaiau,
Heads of swine—gluttons—Alas! and where are they now?
Those that I played with, those that nursed me, those that I nursed?
God, and I outliving them! I, the least and the worst—
I, that thought myself crafty, snared by this herd of swine,
In the tortures of hell and desolate, stripped of all that was mine:
All!—my friends and my fathers—the silver heads of yore
That trooped to the council, the children that ran to the open door
Crying with innocent voices and clasping a father's knees!
And mine, my wife—my daughter—my sturdy climber of trees,
Ah, never to climb again!"

Thus in the dusk of the night,
(For clouds rolled in the sky and the moon was swallowed from sight)
Pacing and gnawing his fists, Rahéro raged by the shore.
Vengeance: that must be his. But much was to do before;
And first a single life to be snatched from a deadly place,
A life, the root of revenge, surviving plant of the race.
And next the race to be raised anew, and the lands of the clan
Repeopled. So Rahéro designed, a prudent man
Even in wrath, and turned for the means of revenge and escape:
A boat to be seized by stealth, a wife to be taken by rape.

Still was the dark lagoon; beyond on the coral wall,
He saw the breakers shine, he heard them bellow and fall.
Alone, on the top of the reef, a man with a flaming brand
Walked, gazing and pausing, a fish-spear poised in his hand.
The foam boiled to his calf when the mightier breakers came,
And the torch shed in the wind scattering tufts of flame.
Afar on the dark lagoon a canoe lay idly at wait:
A figure dimly guiding it: surely the fisherman's mate.
Rahéro saw and he smiled. He straightened his mighty thews:
Naked, with never a weapon, and covered with scorch and bruise,

He straightened his arms, he filled the void of his body
with breath,
And, strong as the wind in his manhood, doomed the
fisher to death.

Silent he entered the water, and silently swam, and came
There where the fisher walked, holding on high the
flame.
Loud on the pier of the reef volleyed the breach of the
sea;
And hard at the back of the man, Rahéro crept to his knee
On the coral, and suddenly sprang and seized him, the
elder hand
Clutching the joint of his throat, the other snatching the
brand
Ere it had time to fall, and holding it steady and high.
Strong was the fisher, brave, and swift of mind and of
eye—
Strongly he threw in the clutch; but Rahéro resisted the
strain,
And jerked, and the spine of life snapped with a crack
in twain,
And the man came slack in his hands and tumbled a lump
at his feet.

One moment: and there, on the reef, where the breakers
whitened and beat,

Rahéro was standing alone, glowing and scorched and bare,
A victor unknown of any, raising the torch in the air.
But once he drank of his breath, and instantly set him to fish
Like a man intent upon supper at home and a savoury dish.
For what should the woman have seen? A man with a torch—and then
A moment's blur of the eyes—and a man with a torch again.
And the torch had scarcely been shaken. "Ah, surely," Rahéro said,
"She will deem it a trick of the eyes, a fancy born in the head;
But time must be given the fool to nourish a fool's belief."
So far a while, a sedulous fisher, he walked the reef,
Pausing at times and gazing, striking at times with the spear:
Lastly, uttered the call; and even as the boat drew near,
Like a man that was done with its use, tossed the torch in the sea.
Lightly he leaped on the boat beside the woman; and she
Lightly addressed him, and yielded the paddle and place to sit;
For now the torch was extinguished the night was black as the pit.

Rahéro set him to row, never a word he spoke,
And the boat sang in the water urged by his vigorous stroke.
"What ails you?" the woman asked, "and why did you drop the brand?
We have only to kindle another as soon as we come to land."
Never a word Rahéro replied, but urged the canoe.
And a chill fell on the woman.—"Atta, speak! is it you?
Speak! Why are you silent? Why do you bend aside?
Wherefore steer to the seaward?" thus she panted and cried.
Never a word from the oarsman, toiling there in the dark;
But right for a gate of the reef he silently headed the bark,
And wielding the single paddle with passionate sweep on sweep,
Drove her, the little fitted, forth on the open deep.

And fear, there where she sat, froze the woman to stone:
Not fear of the crazy boat and the weltering deep alone;
But a keener fear of the night, the dark, and the ghostly hour,
And the thing that drove the canoe with more than a mortal's power
And more than a mortal's boldness. For much she knew of the dead

That haunt and fish upon reefs, toiling like men, for
bread,
And traffic with human fishers, or slay them and take
their ware,
Till the hour when the star of the dead[15] goes down, and
the morning air
Blows, and the cocks are singing on shore. And surely
she knew
The speechless thing at her side belonged to the grave.[16]
It blew
All night from the south; all night, Rahéro contended and
kept
The prow to the cresting sea; and, silent as though she
slept,
The woman huddled and quaked. And now was the peep
of day.
High and long on their left the mountainous island lay;
And over the peaks of Taiárapu arrows of sunlight
struck.
On shore the birds were beginning to sing; the ghostly
ruck
Of the buried had long ago returned to the covered
grave;
And here on the sea, the woman waxing suddenly brave,
Turned her swiftly about and looked in the face of the
man.
And sure he was none that she knew, none of her country
or clan:

A stranger, mother-naked, and marred with the marks of
the fire,
But comely and great of stature, a man to obey and
admire.

And Rahéro regarded her also, fixed, with a frowning
face,
Judging the woman's fitness to mother a warlike race.
Broad of shoulder, ample of girdle, long in the thigh,
Deep of bosom she was, and bravely supported his eye.

"Woman," said he, "last night the men of your folk—
Man, woman, and maid, smothered my race in smoke.
It was done like cowards; and I, a mighty man of my
hands,
Escaped, a single life; and now to the empty lands
And smokeless hearths of my people, sail, with yourself,
alone.
Before your mother was born, the die of today was
thrown
And you selected. Your husband, vainly striving, to fall
Broken between these hands; yourself to be severed from
all,
The places, the people, you love—home, kindred, and
clan—
And to dwell in a dessert and bear the babes of a kinless
man."

NOTES TO THE SONG OF RAHÉRO

[1] *"The aito," quasi* champion, or brave. One skilled in the use of some weapon, who wandered the country challenging distinguished rivals and taking part in local quarrels. It was in the natural course of his advancement to be at last employed by a chief, or king; and it would then be a part of his duties to purvey the victim for sacrifice. One of the doomed families was indicated; the aito took his weapon and went forth alone; a little behind him bearers followed with the sacrificial basket. Sometimes the victim showed fight, sometimes prevailed; more often without doubt, he fell. But whatever body was found, the bearers indifferently took up.

[2] *"Pai," "Honoura,"* and *"Ahupu."* Legendary persons of Tahiti, all natives of Taiárapu. Of the two first, I have collected singular although imperfect legends, which I hope soon to lay before the public in another place. Of Ahupu, except in snatches of song, little memory appears to linger. She dwelt at least about Tepari—"the sea-cliffs,"—the eastern fastness of the isle; walked by paths known only to herself upon the mountains; was courted by dangerous suitors who came swimming from adjacent islands, and defended and rescued (as I gather) by the loyalty of native fish. My anxiety to learn more of "Ahupu Vehine" became (during my stay in Taiárapu) a cause of some diversion to that mirthful people, the inhabitants.

[3] *Covered an oven."* The cooking fire is made in a hole in the ground, and is then buried.

[4] *"Flies."* This is perhaps an anachronism. Even speaking of today in Tahiti, the phrase would have to be understood as referring mainly to mosquitoes, and these only in watered valleys with close woods, such as I suppose to form the surroundings of Rahéro's homestead. Quarter of a mile away, where the air moves freely, you shall look in vain for one.

[5] *"Hook"* of mother-of-pearl. Bright-hook fishing, and that with the spear, appear to the favourite native methods.

[6] *"Leaves,"* the plates of Tahiti.

[7]*"Yottowas,"* so spelled for convenience of pronunciation, *quasi* Tacksmen in the Scottish Highlands. The organisation of eight sub-districts and eight yottowas to a division which was in use (until yesterday) among the Tevas, I have attributed without authority to the next clan.

[8]*"Omare,"* pronounce as a dactyl. A loaded quarter-staff, one of the two favourite weapons of the Tahitian brave: the javelin, or casting spear, was the other.

[9]*"The ribbon of light."* Still to be seen (and heard) spinning from one marae to another on Tahiti; or so I have it upon evidence that would rejoice the Psychical Society.

[10]*"Námunu-úra."* The complete name is Namunu-ura te aropa. Why it should be pronounced Námunu, dactyllically, I cannot see, but so I have always heard it. This was the clan immediately beyond the Tevas on the south coast of the island. At the date of the tale the clan organisation must have been very weak. There is no particular mention of Támatéa's mother going to Papara, to the head chief of her own clan, which would appear her natural recourse. On the other hand, she seems to have visited various lesser chiefs among the Tevas, and these to have excused themselves solely on the danger of the enterprise. The broad distinction here drawn between Nateva and Námunu-úra is therefore not impossibly anachronistic.

[11]*"Hiopa the king."* Hiopa was really the name of the king (chief) of Vaiau; but I could never learn that of the king of Paea—pronounce to rhyme with the Indian *ayah*—and I gave the name where it was most needed. This note must appear otiose indeed to readers who have never heard of either of these two gentlemen; and perhaps there is only one person in the world capable at once of reading my verses and spying the inaccuracy. For him, for Mr. Tati Salmon, hereditary high chief of the Tevas, the note is solely written: a small attention from a clansman to his chief.

[12]*"Let the pigs be tapu."* It is impossible to explain *tapu* in a note: we have it as an English word, taboo. Suffice it, that a thing which was *tapu* must not be touched, nor a place that was *tapu* visited.

[13] *"Fish, the food of desire."* There is a special word in the Tahitian language to signify *hungering after fish.* I may remark that here is one of my chief difficulties about the whole story. How did king, commons, women, and all come to eat together at this feast? But it troubled none of my numerous authorities; so there must certainly be some natural explanation.

[14] *"The mustering word of the clan."*

Teva te na,
Teva te matai!
Teva the wind,
Teva the rain!

[15, 16] *"The star of the dead."* Venus as a morning star. I have collected much curious evidence as to this belief. The dead retain their taste for a fish diet, enter into copartnery with living fishers, and haunt the reef and the lagoon. The conclusion attributed to the nameless lady of the legend would be reached today, under the like circumstances, by ninety per cent of Polynesians; and here I probably understate by one-tenth.

INTRODUCTION

I first heard this legend of my own country from that friend of men of letters, Mr. Alfred Nutt, "there in roaring London's central stream"; and since the ballad first saw the light of day in *Scribner's Magazine,* Mr. Nutt and Lord Archibald Campbell have been in public controversy on the facts. Two clans, the Camerons and the Campbells, lay claim to this bracing story; and they do well: the man who preferred his plighted troth to the commands and menaces of the dead is an ancestor worth disputing. But the Campbells must rest content: they have the broad lands and the broad page of history; this appanage must be denied them; for between the name of *Cameron* and that of *Campbell,* the muse will never hesitate.

TICONDEROGA

A LEGEND OF THE WEST HIGHLANDS

THIS is the tale of the man
  Who heard a word in the night
In the land of the heathery hills,
  In the days of the feud and the fight.
By the sides of the rainy sea,
  Where never a stranger came,
On the awful lips of the dead,
  He heard the outlandish name.
It sang in his sleeping ears,
  It hummed in his waking head:
The name—Ticonderoga,
  The utterance of the dead.

I. THE SAYING OF THE NAME

On the loch-side of Appin,
  When the mist blew from the sea,
A Stewart stood with a Cameron:
  An angry man was he.
The blood beat in his ears,
  The blood ran hot to his head,
The mist blew from the sea,
  And there was the Cameron dead.
"O, what have I done to my friend,
  O, what have I done to mysel',

That he should be cold and dead,
  And I in the danger of all?
Nothing but danger about me,
  Danger behind and before,
Death at wait in the heather
  In Appin and Mamore,
Hate at all of the ferries
  And death at each of the fords,
Camerons priming gunlocks
  And Camerons sharpening swords."

But this was a man of counsel,
  This was a man of a score,

There dwelt no pawkier Stewart
  In Appin or Mamore.
He looked on the blowing mist,
  He looked on the awful dead,
And there came a smile on his face
  And there slipped a thought in his head.

Out over cairn and moss,
  Out over scrog and scaur,
He ran as runs the clansman
  That bears the cross of war.
His heart beat in his body,
  His hair clove to his face,
When he came at last in the gloaming
  To the dead man's brother's place.
The east was white with the moon,
  The west with the sun was red,
And there, in the house-doorway,
  Stood the brother of the dead.

"I have slain a man to my danger,
  I have slain a man to my death.
I put my soul in your hands,"
  The panting Stewart saith.
"I lay it bare in your hands,
  For I know your hands are leal;
And be you my targe and bulwark
  From the bullet and the steel."

Then up and spoke the Cameron,
  And gave him his hand again:
"There shall never a man in Scotland
  Set faith in me in vain:
And whatever man you have slaughtered,
  Of whatever name or line,
By my sword and yonder mountain,
  I make your quarrel mine.
I bid you in to my fireside,
  I share with you house and hall;
It stands upon my honour
  To see you safe from all."

It fell in the time of midnight,
  When the fox barked in the den
And the plaids were over the faces
  In all the houses of men,
That as the living Cameron
  Lay sleepless on his bed,
Out of the night and the other world,
  Came in to him the dead.

"My blood is on the heather,
  My bones are on the hill;
There is joy in the home of ravens
  That the young shall eat their fill.
My blood is poured in the dust,
  My soul is spilled in the air;

And the man that has undone me
  Sleeps in my brother's care."
"I'm wae for your death, my brother,
  But if all of my house were dead,
I couldnae withdraw the plighted hand,
  Or break the word once said."

"O, what shall I say to our father,
  In the place to which I fare?
O, what shall I say to our mother,
  Who greets to see me there?
And to all the kindly Camerons
  That have lived and died long-syne—
Is this the word you send them,
  Fause-hearted brother mine?"

"It's neither fear nor duty,
  It's neither quick nor dead
Shall gar me withdraw the plighted hand,
  Or break the word once said."
Thrice in the time of midnight,
  When the fox barked in the den,
And the plaids were over the faces
  In all the houses of men,
Thrice as the living Cameron
  Lay sleepless on his bed,
Out of the night and the other world
  Came in to him the dead,

And cried to him for vengeance
  On the man that laid him low;
And thrice the living Cameron
  Told the dead Cameron, no.

"Thrice have you seen me, brother,
  But now shall see me no more,
Till you meet your angry fathers
  Upon the farther shore.
Thrice have I spoken, and now,
  Before the cock be heard,
I take my leave forever
  With the naming of a word.
It shall sing in your sleeping ears,
  It shall hum in your waking head,
The name—Ticonderoga,
  And the warning of the dead."

Now when the night was over
  And the time of people's fears,
The Cameron walked abroad,
  And the word was in his ears.
"Many a name I know,
  But never a name like this;
O, where shall I find a skilly man
  Shall tell me what it is?"

With many a man he counselled

Of high and low degree,
With the herdsmen on the mountains
And the fishers of the sea.
And he came and went unweary,
And read the books of yore,
And the runes that were written of old
On stones upon the moor.
And many a name he was told,
But never the name of his fears—
Never, in east or west,
The name that rang in his ears:
Names of men and of clans,
Names for the grass and the tree,
For the smallest tarn in the mountains,
The smallest reef in the sea:
Names for the high and low,
The names of the craig and the flat;
But in all the land of Scotland,
Never a name like that.

II. THE SEEKING OF THE NAME

And now there was speech in the south,
And a man of the south that was wise,
A periwig'd lord of London,
Called on the clans to rise.
And the riders rode, and the summons
Came to the western shore,

To the land of the sea and the heather,
  To Appin and Mamore.
It called on all to gather
  From every scrog and scaur,
That loved their fathers' tartan
  And the ancient game of war.
And down the watery valley
  And up the windy hill,
Once more, as in the olden,
  The pipes were sounding shrill;
Again in highland sunshine
  The naked steel was bright;
And the lads, once more in tartan,
  Went forth again to fight.

"O, why should I dwell here
  With a weird upon my life,
When the clansmen shout for battle
  And the war-swords clash in strife?
I cannae joy at feast,
  I cannae sleep in bed,
For the wonder of the word
  And the warning of the dead.
It sings in my sleeping ears,
  It hums in my waking head,
The name—Ticonderoga,
  The utterance of the dead.
Then up, and with the fighting men

To march away from here,
Till the cry of the great war-pipe
Shall drown it in my ear!"

Where flew King George's ensign
The plaided soldiers went:
They drew the sword in Germany,
In Flanders pitched the tent.
The bells of foreign cities
Rang far across the plain:
They passed the happy Rhine,
They drank the rapid Main.
Through Asiatic jungles
The Tartans filed their way,
And the neighing of the war-pipes
Struck terror in Cathay.
"Many a name have I heard," he thought,
"In all the tongues of men,
Full many a name both here and there,
Full many both now and then.
When I was at home in my father's house
In the land of the naked knee,
Between the eagles that fly in the lift
And the herrings that swim in the sea,
And now that I am a captain-man
With a braw cockade in my hat—
Many a name have I heard," he thought,
"But never a name like that."

III. THE PLACE OF THE NAME

There fell a war in a woody place,
  Lay far across the sea,
A war of the march in the mirk midnight
  And the shot from behind the tree,
The shaven head and the painted face,
  The silent foot in the wood,
In a land of a strange, outlandish tongue
  That was hard to be understood.

It fell about the gloaming
  The general stood with his staff,
He stood and he looked east and west
  With little mind to laugh.
"Far have I been and much have I seen,
  And kent both gain and loss,
But here we have woods on every hand
  And a kittle water to cross.
Far have I been and much have I seen,
  But never the beat of this:
And there's one must go down to that waterside
  To see how deep it is."

It fell in the dusk of the night
  When unco things betide,
The skilly captain, the Cameron,
  Went down to that waterside.

Canny and soft the captain went;
  And a man of the woody land,
With the shaven head and the painted face,
  Went down at his right hand.
It fell in the quiet night,
  There was never a sound to ken;
But all of the woods to the right and the left
  Lay filled with the painted men.

"Far have I been and much have I seen,
  Both as a man and boy,
But never have I set forth a foot
  On so perilous an employ."

It fell in the dusk of the night
  When unco things betide,
That he was aware of a captain-man
  Drew near to the waterside.
He was aware of his coming
  Down in the gloaming alone;
And he looked in the face of the man
  And lo! the face was his own.

"This is my weird," he said,
  "And now I ken the worst;
For many shall fall the morn,
  But I shall fall with the first.
O, you of the outland tongue,

You of the painted face,
This is the place of my death;
Can you tell me the name of the place?"

"Since the Frenchmen have been here
They have called it Sault-Marie;
But that is a name for priests,
And not for you and me.
It went by another word,"
Quoth he of the shaven head:
"It was called Ticonderoga
In the days of the great dead."
And it fell on the morrow's morning,
In the fiercest of the fight,
That the Cameron bit the dust
As he foretold at night;
And far from the hills of heather,
Far from the isles of the sea,
He sleeps in the place of the name
As it was doomed to be.